LC 11/5/59.

METHUEN'S
MONOGRAPHS ON
PHYSICAL SUBJECTS

General Editor B. L. WORSNOP, B.Sc., Ph.D.

THE COSMIC RADIATION

THE COSMIC RADIATION

J. E. HOOPER
Rask-Ørsted Fellow,

and

M. SCHARFF
Research Assistant,

both of Institute for Theoretical Physics
University of Copenhagen

LONDON: METHUEN & CO LTD
NEW YORK: JOHN WILEY & SONS INC

First published in 1958

CATALOGUE NO 4068/U

© *1958 J. E. Hooper and M. Scharff*
Printed in Great Britain
by Butler and Tanner Ltd, Frome and London

Preface

This little book had its origin in a series of lectures given here by one of us. Its purpose is to provide an introduction to the subject suitable for students and physicists engaged in other fields. It has been necessary to restrict the subject-matter to a sketch of the properties of the primary radiation, and the development of the radiation in its passage through the atmosphere, omitting detailed discussion of more particular subjects, such as the fluctuations of the intensity with time and extensive air showers. At the same time, it has not been thought suitable to burden the text with detailed references to original work. Instead, we have included in the list of 'Further Reading' on page 165 a number of books and review articles which contain extensive bibliographies. Our indebtedness to the authors of these books and reviews will be obvious and is gratefully acknowledged.

We would like to take this opportunity of thanking the many authors and publishers who have given us permission to reproduce diagrams and photographs. Individual acknowledgement is made in the texts to the appropriate figures.

Universitetets Institut for Teoretisk Fysik,
Blegdamsvej, 17,
Copenhagen.

J. E. H.
M. S.

January, 1957

Contents

Plates

CHAPTER 1

Introduction

The discovery of the existence of a high energy cosmic radiation (i.e. a radiation reaching the earth from outside the immediate solar system) was a consequence of certain experiments undertaken at the end of the last century and the beginning of the present century, on the conductivity of gases. This work had shown that the conductivity of a gas was increased when it was exposed to high energy radiation, as, for example, that produced by radioactive substances. It was believed, on theoretical grounds, that a gas should be non-conducting in the absence of radiation, provided that the potential gradient across it was not so high that sparking could take place. In order to test this hypothesis experiments were undertaken in which the conductivity was measured after attempts had been made to shield the gas from all possible external sources of radiation. It was, however, found that there always remained a residual ionization of about 10 ion pairs/cm.³/sec. in dry air at N.T.P. Various suggestions were advanced to explain this phenomenon; among them, residual radioactivity of the shielding materials, and spontaneous ionization due to the thermal motion of the gas molecules.

That these explanations were not sufficient to account for the observed phenomena was shown by the experiments of Göckel, Hess, and Kolhörster, who, in the years immediately prior to 1914, sent suitable ionization chambers up with balloons, and measured the variation of the conductivity of the contained gas as a function of altitude. They were able to show that the conductivity, and hence the ionization produced in the gas, decreased up to an altitude of about 2,000 feet above sea-level, and thereafter increased steadily up to the highest altitudes which their balloons reached (30,000 feet), where it was many times greater than at sea-level. From this experimental result it was clear that the whole of the residual ionization observed at sea-level could not be due to the radioactivity of the earth, nor can it be a property of the gas with which the ionization chamber is filled. Thus, Hess was led to propose the existence of a very penetrating ionizing radiation which enters the earth's atmosphere from outer space. The radiation must be extremely penetrating for it is able to penetrate the whole of the earth's atmosphere. That the immediate source of the radiation is not the sun is a consequence of the fact that the observations showed that any diurnal variations which exist must be very small, so that the phenomenon came eventually to be called the cosmic radiation.

Although the above conclusions were reached by a number of physicists in the years immediately prior to the outbreak of the first World War in 1914, it was not until 1926 that the existence of the cosmic radiation was generally accepted. Scepticism was due to two main causes. First, the instrumentation used for the early experiments was not always absolutely reliable, so that there was always some room for doubt about the interpretation of the experimental results. Secondly, the interpretation of the data obtained on the absorption of the radiation was rendered very difficult by the so-called transition effects which the radiation displays when it passes from a less dense to a more dense absorber. These effects led to apparently contradictory results when attempts were made to measure the absorption coefficient of the radiation by different methods which were expected, on the basis of what had previously been learnt about the absorption of radioactive radiations, to yield the same answer.

At the time of Hess's and Kolhörster's first experiments the most penetrating form of radiation known was the γ-radiation from radioactive elements. Kolhörster found that the absorption of the cosmic radiation in the atmosphere was about 10^{-5} cm.$^{-1}$ in air at N.T.P., or nearly an order of magnitude smaller than that of the γ-radiation. On the other hand, experiments with lead-shielded chambers showed that the absorption of the radiation in the first few centimetres of lead thickness was not very different from that to be expected from γ-radiation. The apparent contradiction was not resolved until more detailed experiments were made and the complicated transition effect was found. After rapid absorption in the first 10 cm. of lead, there remained a component of the radiation which was even more penetrating than the measurements on the height-intensity curve showed the total radiation to be. These experiments were checked against others in which the absorption of the radiation in glacier ice and in mountain-lake water was measured. In both of these experiments the background radioactivity from the absorbing substance could be expected to be particularly low.

The establishment of the existence of the cosmic radiation did not in itself clarify the problem as to its nature. In view of its great penetrating power many workers believed that it must consist of very high energy photons, which were the most penetrating form of radiation known at that time. The problems which were now raised had to be tackled with more refined instruments than had been available at the time of the earlier measurements for which the ionization chamber had been used. In the meantime, however, a number of different types of radiation detectors had been developed within the field of nuclear physics. While the ionization chamber could measure the integrated ionization produced by the passage of the radiation, the Geiger–Müller counter was capable of being discharged by the passage of a single charged particle or γ-ray quantum. The efficiencies in these two instances are rather widely different, for the charged particle discharges the counter by means of the ionization which it produces directly, while the γ-ray quantum does so by virtue of the ionization produced by secondary electrons, to which it loses part of its energy in Compton scatters. Thus, a counter detects γ-rays with an efficiency which is about 1 per cent. of that with which it detects the passage of charged particles. By using two counters, which are connected to an amplifying circuit in such a way that a count is recorded only when they are both discharged 'simultaneously', one may record the passage of fast charged particles. The two counters are said to be operated in coincidence, and the arrangement is called a counter-telescope, because it only registers that portion of the total radiation which arrives from directions lying within a chosen angular interval, determined by the dimensions of the counters and the distance between them.

The other instrument introduced into cosmic ray physics at the end of the twenties was the Wilson cloud chamber, which was not only capable of detecting individual charged particles but also of giving much more detailed information on their trajectories and interactions than the Geiger–Müller counter. This is particularly true when it is used in conjunction with a powerful magnetic field, which enables the momenta of the individual particles to be measured.

One of the first results of the introduction of these two new instruments into cosmic ray research was the discovery that a large proportion of the radiation, both at sea-level and at higher altitudes, consisted of charged particles. In the following decade two new types of fundamental particle were found to exist among the cosmic rays: the positron, or positive electron, and the μ-meson, and a vast groundwork of experimental fact was established, which enabled very rapid improvements in the knowledge of the radiation to be made at the end of the second World War. The rapid progress achieved during the past ten years has also been assisted very greatly by the introduction of a third new particle detector: the nuclear emulsion.

Once the existence of the radiation was established, work on its properties was greatly intensified, and, in particular, very much more careful studies were made on its absorption in various substances, in the hope of discovering in detail

the nature of the radiation. Thus, in 1926 Hoffmann discovered that the absorption in lead underwent a transition
at a thickness of lead of about 10 cm., after which thickness
the absorption coefficient dropped very sharply. A typical
absorption curve is shown in Fig. 1. This experiment led to
the phenomenological division of the cosmic radiation into
two components: an easily absorbed, or soft component,
and a penetrating or hard component.

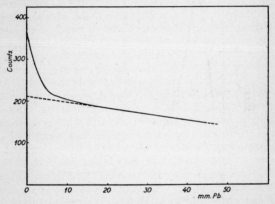

FIG. 1. The absorption of the sea-level cosmic radiation in
lead. (From Auger *et al.*, *J. de Phys. et Rad.*, 7, 58 (1936))

In many of the early cloud-chamber photographs it was
noticed that groups of particles appeared to enter the
chamber simultaneously and with approximately the same
directions of motion, so that they often seemed to originate
from some common point outside the chamber. When one
or more lead plates were placed across the chamber it was
found that these 'shower' particles were capable of producing further showers of particles when they passed
through an absorbing material. This effect was in marked
contrast to that produced by the particles which entered

the chamber singly, which generally passed through several lead plates without producing any form of interaction.

The existence of shower-producing particles was also

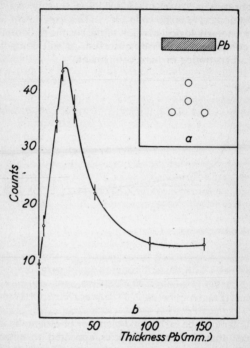

FIG. 2. Typical counter arrangement used for the study of the shower transition curve (*a*) and the curve obtained with it (*b*). (From Auger *et al.*, *J. de Phys. et Rad.*, 7, 58 (1936))

demonstrated by Rossi using an arrangement of counters similar to that sketched in Fig. 2*a*. The counters are connected in coincidence, and measurements are made of the rate of threefold and fourfold coincidences as a function of the thickness of the lead. In an arrangement of this sort there is a finite count for zero lead thickness caused by showers which have been formed higher in the atmosphere reaching the apparatus. Rossi, and many others after him, found that the number of coincidences at first increased with increasing lead thickness, and then, after a sharp maximum, decreased very slowly for thickness of lead greater than 10 cm. (Fig. 2b). It did not sink to zero, even with very great thicknesses of lead. From this one can conclude that the average number of particles produced in the shower increases at first as the thickness of the lead is increased, but, when the energy of the parent particle becomes sufficiently dissipated among the secondaries, these will be absorbed by the lead. The fact that even with very great thickness of absorber the number of showers does not sink to zero could be supposed to be a result of the particles of the very penetrating component occasionally producing a secondary which could, in turn, produce a shower in the lead.

The phenomenon of shower production leads to a rapid degradation and dissipation of the energy of the incoming particle, and one is thus led to identify the shower-producing particles with the soft component. Rossi's experiment had already demonstrated that the shower-producing particles can be secondary to the penetrating component, which explains how it is possible that there should still exist a soft component at sea-level, and measurements of the shower intensity show the same dependence on altitude as does the intensity of the soft component, found by taking the difference between the total intensity and that of the hard component measured with shielded counters.

The shower-producing particles were early identified as electrons, and the qualitative aspects of the phenomena observed were made clear by the discovery of the positive electron by Anderson in 1932, and by the cloud-chamber photographs of Blackett and Occhialini which showed positive and negative electrons emerging from lead plates in showers. From these photographs, which were interpreted in the light of Dirac's theory of the positive electron, it was understood that the shower was built up of a number of steps of two different kinds. (1) A fast electron radiates high energy photons when it is deflected by the coulomb fields of the nuclei of the absorber (*Bremsstrahlung*). (2) High energy photons interact in the coulomb fields of nuclei and give all their energy to the formation of a pair of positive and negative electrons (pair production).

A few years later, in 1935, Bhabha and Heitler, and, independently, Carlson and Oppenheimer, published a detailed mathematical treatment of the shower process based on the Dirac quantum electrodynamics.

The nature of the penetrating component of the radiation at sea-level presented a more intractable problem. While it was known that the probability for *Bremsstrahlung* was inversely proportional to the square of the mass of the incident particle, so that protons and heavier particles could not be expected to lose energy by cascade shower production, it was also expected that they would interact strongly with the nuclei of the atoms of the absorbing materials through which they passed, losing a very considerable proportion of their energy in each encounter. The absorption of the hard component, on the other hand, corresponds to the energy loss of singly charged particles of very great energy by ionization alone.

This problem was solved by the discovery of the μ-meson by Anderson and Neddermeyer, and, independently, by Street and Stevenson in 1937. These particles, which were found to have a mass of about 200 times that of the electron, and which were unstable against decay into an electron and one or more neutral particles with a proper half-life of about two microseconds, were in many respects very similar to those which had been predicted by Yukawa to explain nuclear forces, and were, indeed, at first identified with them. It was found, however, that they differed in one very important respect. Yukawa's particles were expected to interact strongly with nuclear matter, while the experimental evidence showed that the interaction of μ-mesons was very weak. Thus, they could only lose energy by ionization and elastic collision processes; a property which we have seen was necessary in order to explain the low absorption of the penetrating component.

While the existence of the μ-meson provided a satisfactory explanation of the properties of the hard component, attempts to fit it into the Yukawa formalism were disappointed, due to the contradiction between the experimental results and the theory on the strength of its interaction with nuclear matter. These difficulties were eventually partially solved by the discovery of the π-meson by Powell and his co-workers in 1947. The π-meson, which was found to be 1·32 times heavier than the μ-meson, was shown to be strongly interacting, and to decay with the emission of a μ-meson and a neutrino. Powell's group were further able to demonstrate that π-mesons were in fact directly created in very high energy nuclear collisions of the primary radiation near the top of the atmosphere. The hard component at sea-level could be shown to be composed of the μ-mesons produced by decay in flight of energetic π-mesons high in the atmosphere. The lifetime of the π-mesons was shown to be about 100 times shorter than that of the μ-mesons, so that, although the π-mesons are strongly interacting, few of them have time to interact before they decay.

The other very important field of cosmic ray research during the late twenties and thirties was the study of the intensity of the radiation and its variations with the place and time of observation. The geomagnetic latitude effect was discovered by Clay in 1931 and the east–west effect by Johnson and Young in the following year. The existence of these effects showed that the primary radiation must consist largely of charged particles, and that the majority of these must be positively charged.

Time variations in intensity were found to be small,

B

leading to the conclusion that the immediate source of the radiation is not within the solar system, but the correlation between certain large irregular fluctuations and the appearance of large solar flares has led to the idea that the sun is in fact responsible for at least a part of the low energy radiation. Other effects, of more interest to the interpretation of the processes taking place within the atmosphere, are the barometer effect; the correlation of the intensity of the radiation with the barometric pressure at the place of observation: and the temperature effect, which is the correlation of the intensity with the temperature of the overlying layers of air, or, in other words, with the effective density of the atmosphere. That there should be a temperature effect at all is a direct consequence of the instability of the μ-meson.

CHAPTER 2

Experimental Techniques

Detection of particles

The particle detectors used in the study of the cosmic radiation are all based on the effect of ionization produced by a charged particle when traversing some sensitive volume in the detector. Neutral particles are detected indirectly, in the sense that one registers only the charged secondaries from some process, such as pair creation (by γ-rays) or (n, p) or (n, α) nuclear reactions (by neutrons). The detecting instruments may be roughly divided into two classes: those that record electronically the ionization produced by the traversing particle—ionization chambers and counters; and those that render visible the trajectory of the particle—the cloud chamber and the photographic emulsion. In each of these broad categories there are a number of subdivisions depending upon the type of measurement for which the instrument was designed.

The earliest observations of the cosmic radiation were performed with the *ionization chamber*. This is a gasfilled chamber with two internal electrodes. Between these is maintained a potential difference, just sufficient to ensure that the ions produced in the chamber are drawn to the electrodes before recombination can take place. Under these conditions the *saturation current* between the electrodes is proportional to the number of ions produced in the chamber per unit time and volume. Usually the current induced by a single traversing particle is too small to be measured, and the ionization chamber is therefore operated with a circuit, the relaxation time of which is long compared to the average interval between the arrival of the individual particles. The current is then proportional to the average total rate of ionization in the chamber, and the instrument can therefore give information on the cosmic ray intensities. It must be remembered, however, that strictly speaking the ionization chamber measures a very special property of the radiation (the ionizing power), and that it gives no direct information on the number of particles traversing the chamber or on their properties and relative abundance.

Further progress in the study of cosmic radiation was therefore dependent on the development of instruments and methods which made it possible to detect single particles, to determine their velocity and to identify them by measuring their mass and charge. In the later sections of this chapter we shall discuss briefly the most important techniques now in use. First, however, we shall consider in the next section some of the general principles which form the basis of particle identification by means of their particular behaviour in the detecting instrument. The physical quantities met with here are also useful in the analysis of the penetration of cosmic radiation into the earth's atmosphere.

The observable effects produced by fast charged particles

When an atomic particle of charge $z_1 e$ traverses a detecting instrument two kinds of information may be had from the *shape* of the trajectory. If the detector is placed in a magnetic field of strength H one may determine, by measuring the radius of curvature, ρ, the magnetic rigidity, $H\rho$, which is proportional to p/z_1, the particle momentum per unit charge. For simplicity we here consider a magnetic field perpendicular to the trajectory.

However, if the particle is not moving *in vacuo* the ideal circular orbit is somewhat perturbed by collisions with the atoms in the detector. The resulting scattering restricts the accuracy with which ρ may be determined, and when the density of matter in the sensitive volume is high, the magnetic deflection may be masked by the accumulated effect of the numerous atomic collisions. Thus, in the analysis of particles penetrating solids or liquids, the magnetic field is usually of little importance as the trajectory is determined in a statistical way by the *multiple scattering*. Fortunately, this effect in itself provides another source of knowledge of the properties of the traversing particle.

In the individual collisions with atomic nuclei of charge number Z the differential cross-section for an angular deflection ξ is given by the Rutherford formula, which, for small values of ξ, reduces to:

$$d\sigma = \frac{8\pi z_1{}^2 Z^2 e^4}{p^2 v^2} \cdot \frac{d\xi}{\xi^3}, \qquad (2.1)$$

where p and v are the momentum and velocity, respectively, of the incoming particle. On a section of track of length Δ, in matter of atomic density N, the average number of deflections between ξ and $\xi + d\xi$ is then $N\Delta d\sigma$. The individual deflections will occur with equal probability for all azimuthal angles with respect to the particle velocity, and the total deflection, Ξ_Δ, will therefore on the average be zero. The distribution around this mean value is to a first approximation gaussian, and the width is given by the mean square deviation $\langle \Xi_\Delta{}^2 \rangle$, which can be shown to be the sum of the square deflections in the individual collisions: $\langle \Xi_\Delta{}^2 \rangle = N\Delta \int_{\xi_{\text{min.}}}^{\xi_{\text{max.}}} \xi^2 \, d\sigma$, or:

$$\langle \Xi_\Delta{}^2 \rangle = \frac{8\pi z_1{}^2 Z^2 e^4}{p^2 v^2} N . \Delta \ln\left(\frac{\xi_{\text{max.}}}{\xi_{\text{min.}}}\right). \qquad (2.2)$$

In this formula the limits of integration, $\xi_{\text{max.}}$ and $\xi_{\text{min.}}$, take account of the breakdown of the simple relation (2.1) in collisions where the particle comes either very close to the nucleus or passes by at a very great distance. In the latter instance the breakdown is due to the screening effect of atomic electrons which cancel the nuclear coulomb field at distances great compared to atomic dimensions. To correct for the screening in a simple way one makes a sharp cut-off of the coulomb field at a distance $\hbar^2/m_e e^2 . Z^{-1/3}$, which is a suitable measure of the extension of the electronic charge distribution. The corresponding deflection may then be taken as the lower limit, $\xi_{min.}$, in formula (2.2).

The value of $\xi_{max.}$ may be determined from considerations of the finite size of the nucleus and the size of the quantum mechanical wave packets involved in the collision, together with the mass of the particle relative to that of the nucleus. Quite often, however, the upper limit of deflections which contribute to multiple scattering is determined by the experimental procedure. Very large deflections show up as sharp bends in the track of the particle, and such 'single scatters' may, according to the conventions of measurement adopted, be omitted in the calculation of the mean square value $\langle \Xi_\Delta^2 \rangle'$ of the observed deflection Ξ_Δ. The value of $\xi_{max.}$ must then be calculated from the convention used. If, for example, in a path length Δ one omits single scatters larger than, say, four times the root mean square angle $\sqrt{\langle \Xi_\Delta^2 \rangle'}$, the value of $\xi_{max.}$ is implicitly given by the equation $\xi_{max.} = 4\sqrt{\langle \Xi_\Delta^2 \rangle}$. Although the ratio $\xi_{max.}/\xi_{min.}$ may thus depend on such quantities as z_1, Z, v, p, and $N\Delta$, the fact that the logarithmic factor is, in most cases, of the order of 10, results in its not being very sensitive to the exact value of the argument, and one may, for many purposes, assume that $\ln (\xi_{max.}/\xi_{min.})$ is a constant.

The experimental determination of pv from multiple scattering is based on formula (2.2). The track of the particle is divided into cells of equal length Δ, the angular deflection Ξ_Δ is measured for each cell, and one then defines a *multiple scattering parameter*, $\bar{\alpha}_\Delta$, which is some suitable average of the measured deflections. The definition may be

$$\bar{\alpha}_\Delta = \sqrt{\langle \Xi_\Delta^2 \rangle'},$$

in which case the value of pv can be found directly by equating $\bar{\alpha}_\Delta^2$ to the right-hand side of (2.2). Usually, however, one measures only the projection of the angles on a plane, and the deflection per cell may be measured either between tangents or chords to the track. The definition of $\bar{\alpha}_\Delta$ may also be changed if one introduces the arithmetic mean of the numerical deflections instead of the root mean square, or if one omits single scatters. All these values of $\bar{\alpha}_\Delta$, though defined in different ways, differ from $\sqrt{\langle \Xi_\Delta{}^2 \rangle}$ only by numerical factors of order unity, and one has therefore the general approximate relation:

$$\bar{\alpha}_\Delta \approx C \frac{z_1}{pv} \Delta^{1/2},$$

where C depends only on the scattering substance and the definition of $\bar{\alpha}$. C is called the scattering constant and it is usually determined for each detecting instrument by calibration experiments with particles of known pv/z_1.

We shall now forget the shape of the track and consider some observable quantities which are associated with the energy loss of a particle penetrating matter. A complete discussion of such effects is far outside the scope of this book, but we shall try to make plausible the most important features.

In the above discussion of scattering we have talked only of the deflection in the coulomb field of the atomic nuclei. It is true that the penetrating particle will also be scattered by the atomic electrons, but as the cross-section per electron is given by (2.1) with $Z = 1$, it is seen that the total contribution from the Z electrons is only $1/Z$ times that from the nucleus, and the former may therefore be neglected for penetration in heavier substances. In the problem of energy loss the situation is completely reversed; the electronic collisions usually being responsible for practically all the energy loss. The reason for this is that the small mass of the electron implies that, for a given momentum transfer, a large transfer of energy is involved. The struck electrons may be expelled from the atom which is then left ionized, whereas in the less violent collisions the atom is only raised to an excited state of energy. The energy lost by both processes is called 'ionization energy loss' or 'collision loss' as opposed to energy loss at high energy by *Bremsstrahlung* (Chapter 5), or the energy loss at extremely small velocities, where energy is transferred only by elastic collisions to translatory motion of the struck atoms.

Let us now consider a heavy atomic particle (i.e. not an electron) of charge number z_1 moving with a not too small velocity v. An electron at a distance q from the path will feel the coulomb force $f \approx z_1 e^2/q^2$ for a short time interval Δt, when the particle is passing by. This 'collision time' may be taken to be $\Delta t \approx 2q/v$, and the momentum, Δp, transferred to the electron is then given by the product $f . \Delta t \approx 2z_1 e^2/qv$. For symmetry reasons Δp is perpendicular to the momentum p of the particle, and its very small deflection is therefore $\Delta p/p = z_1 e^2/pvq$, which may be neglected in the present discussion. It should be noted, however, that from such a simple estimate of the deflection one can deduce formula (2.1).

The transfer of energy is $\Delta T = \dfrac{(\Delta p)^2}{2m_e} \approx 2z_1^2 e^4/m_e v^2 q^2$, which enables us to discuss various observable quantities. Among these the simplest to calculate is the density of δ-rays, n_δ, i.e. the number of fast secondary electrons per unit length of track. These, if sufficiently energetic, may produce observable tracks, the so-called δ-ray tracks, which can be counted according to appropriately chosen conventions. Let now E' be the lower limit of energy of electrons accepted as δ-rays. The corresponding upper limit of the impact parameter q is then given by the above relation, and one finds, in a substance of electronic density NZ,

$$n_\delta = \pi q^2(E') . NZ = NZ \frac{2\pi z_1^2 e^4}{m_e v^2} \frac{1}{E'}. \qquad (2.3)$$

This formula is correct even at high energy, where the problem should be treated relativistically. The reason for this can be understood from a closer analysis of our original line of argument: When $\gamma = (1 - v^2/c^2)^{-1/2}$ is larger than unity the coulomb field acting on the electron is contracted in the direction of motion of the particle, causing a shortening of the collision time by a factor of γ. However, the electric field strength is increased by the same factor, so that the momentum transfer $\Delta p = f.\Delta t$, and therefore also the energy transfer, has an unchanged dependence on q.

We shall now turn to the problem of the *specific energy loss*, i.e. the average loss of energy per unit path length. The number of collisions with impact parameter between q and $q + dq$ is, per unit length, $2\pi q.dq.NZ$, and the specific energy loss is accordingly:

$$\frac{dE}{dx} = 2\pi ZN \int_{q_{min.}}^{q_{max.}} \Delta T(q)qdq = \frac{4\pi z_1{}^2 e^4}{m_e v^2} ZN \ln\left(\frac{q_{max.}}{q_{min.}}\right). \quad (2.4)$$

The situation here is closely analogous to that met with in the calculation of $\langle \Xi_\Delta{}^2 \rangle$: the expression is kept convergent by introducing the limits $q_{max.}$ and $q_{min.}$. The upper one is determined by the binding of the atomic electrons. It may be shown that if the collision time, $2q/v\gamma$, is much larger than $1/\omega_i$, where ω_i is the 'revolution' frequency of the ith electron, then the process becomes adiabatic, and no energy is transferred to the electron. Thus we may choose $q_{i\,max.} \approx v\gamma/\omega_i$, but as this quantity depends upon the frequency of the electron considered, one must average over the atomic frequencies in formula 2·4. In this way we obtain $q_{max.} \approx v\gamma/\bar{\omega}$, where $\bar{\omega}$ is an average frequency defined by the relation $\ln \bar{\omega} = 1/Z \sum_{i=1}^{Z} \ln \omega_i$. The corresponding energy, $\hbar\bar{\omega}$, is called the average excitation potential of the atom in question.

The choice of the lower limit, $q_{min.}$, must correct for our not having used a proper quantum-mechanical treatment. In the centre of mass system the colliding particles will have a wavelength $\lambdabar \approx \hbar/m_e v\gamma$ and, as a smaller geometric cross-section than $\approx \lambdabar^2$ is not significant, we take

$q_{min.} \approx \mathrm{\lambda} \approx \hbar/m_e v \gamma$. For the logarithmic factor we therefore find $\ln(q_{max.}/q_{min.}) \approx \ln(m_e v^2 . \gamma^2/\hbar \bar{\omega})$, and introducing this in (2.4) we arrive at a formula which deviates only slightly from the precise Bethe–Bloch formula:

$$\frac{dE}{dx} = \frac{4\pi z_1^2 e^4}{m_e v^2} ZN \left[\ln\left(\frac{2m_e v^2 \gamma^2}{\hbar \bar{\omega}}\right) - (v/c)^2 \right]. \quad (2.5)$$

A precise calculation of the average excitation potential is very complicated and has only been carried out for atomic

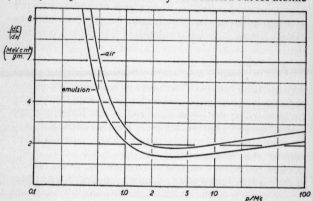

FIG. 3. The rate of energy loss due to the collisions of singly charged particles as a function of p/Mc, where M is the rest mass of the particle

hydrogen and helium. For other substances it is determined empirically by fitting (2.5) to experimental values of dE/dx, and in this way it has been found that for heavier atoms $\hbar \bar{\omega}$ is well approximated by $I_0 . Z$, where $I_0 = 10 - 12$ eV. For fast particles the logarithmic term is large ($\approx 9 - 10$ when $\gamma \approx 2$), and the value of dE/dx is therefore little influenced by a small uncertainty in the magnitude of $\hbar \bar{\omega}$. In Fig. 3 is shown the calculated variation of specific energy loss with normalized momentum, $p/Mc = v\gamma/c$, for singly charged particles penetrating air and photographic emulsion. With increasing momentum the energy loss decreases rapidly, passes through a minimum at $p/Mc \approx 3$, and then rises slowly again with further increase of momentum. This so-called 'relativistic rise' is due to the γ^2 in the logarithmic term of (2.5), and it will be understood from the previous discussion that half of the rise originates in an increase of $q_{max.}$, the other half in a decrease of $q_{min.}$. It can be shown, however, that owing to polarization effects $q_{max.}$ cannot exceed a certain limit, depending only on the density of electrons in the stopping medium; the contribution from distant collisions to the relativistic rise in dE/dx saturates therefore at some high value of γ. This *density effect* has not been included in Fig. 3.

From the point of view of track analysis in particle detectors the most important property of formula (2.5) is that the energy loss does not depend on the mass of the moving particle. Thus, for a given substance, one may write the specific energy loss as $dE/dx = z_1^2 f(v)$, where $f(v)$ is a function only of v, and a relation of this type holds for several other related observables. One is the δ-ray density already considered; another is the specific ionization, I, defined as the number of ion pairs produced by the penetrating particle per unit path length. Empirically it is found that I is closely proportional to dE/dx, so that the energy spent per ion pair is about 20–30 eV., independent of the nature and velocity of the incoming particle. However, when the term specific ionization, or just ionization, is used in connexion with track analysis it may have different meanings, depending on the experiment considered. It may be taken as the number of droplets (in a cloud chamber) or silver grains (in a photographic emulsion) per unit path length. These quantities are also roughly proportional to the specific energy loss, but there are deviations from strict proportionality. One of these arises from the fact that in very violent collisions the struck electron is ejected as a fast δ-ray, and the energy lost by the particle in such collisions can therefore not contribute to the formation of droplets or grains close to the trajectory. For this reason the relativistic rise in the density of grains or droplets includes only the contribution from distant collisions; it saturates at some high value of γ, causing a constant high energy plateau for the grain or droplet density (see Fig. 9).

Irrespective of such detailed considerations of these quantities, one may say quite generally that they will be given by some weighted average of the various energy transfers, the weight function being determined by the mechanism involved in the formation of droplets or grains. From the above treatment of energy loss it is therefore clear that the expression for I will still be some function of v, multiplied by z_1^2, and, loosely speaking, the term ionization is used for any observable quantity with this property.

The validity of this simple behaviour for the specific energy loss enables us to find a simple expression for the residual range, R, of the particle. R is the distance traversed by the particle before it is completely stopped. As the energy is given by the mass, M, of the moving particle, multiplied by a function of v, we find $dR/dv = \dfrac{M}{z_1^2} f_1(v)$, and consequently:

$$R = \frac{M}{z_1^2} f_2(v), \qquad (2.6)$$

where $f_1(v)$ and $f_2(v)$ are functions of v which can be calculated from (2.5) by using the expression for the energy: $E = M(1 - (v/c)^2)^{-1/2}$. In Fig. 42 ($a$ & b) on page 168 are shown the calculated range-energy curves for protons in air, photographic emulsion and lead. The curves may be applied also to other particles by conversion according to formula (2.6), which implies, for particles of equal charge and velocity, the simple relation $M_1/M_2 = R_1/R_2$.

It should be remembered, however, that the above formulae do not apply to electrons, partly because the energy loss for electrons deviates slightly from that given by (2.5), and partly because at high energies the process of *Bremsstrahlung* is, for electrons, much more important than the ionization energy loss. The energy loss by *Bremsstrahlung* is discussed in more detail in Chapter 5, where it is shown that the electron energy on the average decreases exponentially with path length, but with large statistical fluctuations arising from the frequent loss of large amounts of energy in single collisions. This fact, combined with the violent multiple scattering of even fast electrons, implies that the concept of range is not relevant to the slowing down of electrons.

For heavier particles it is worth pointing out that the calculated values of range are not significant if they are much larger than the mean free path for nuclear inter-actions, in which the primary may split the struck nucleus and transfer part of its energy to the fragments. As we shall see, such processes are very important when the primary cosmic radiation enters the earth's atmosphere.

We shall finally discuss one quantity which depends, in a given substance, only on the velocity of the incoming particle. The contribution from distant collisions to the relativistic rise in energy loss is actually due to energy given off as coherent electromagnetic radiation from atoms along the track. We shall not discuss the problems of intensity and spectral distribution for this so-called *Čerenkov radiation*, but only note that the angle of emission, ψ, with respect to the particle trajectory is a measure of the velocity v. The phase velocity of the radiation is $c/n(v)$, where $n(v)$ is the index of refraction of the stopping medium for the frequency considered, and the condition of coherence is therefore:

$$\cos \psi_v = \frac{c}{n(v) \cdot v} = \frac{1}{n(v)\beta}. \qquad (2.7)$$

This simple formula relates the velocity, v, to the angle, ψ, and it shows further that the emission of Čerenkov radia-tion of frequency v is only possible at sufficiently high velocity, where $\beta > 1/n(v)$.

To summarize our discussion in this section we shall list the different observable quantities for a particle of mass M, charge z_1 and velocity $\beta = v/c$:

Magnetic rigidity
$$H\rho = \frac{M}{z_1} \frac{\beta}{\sqrt{1-\beta^2}}$$

Multiple scattering parameter
$$\bar{\alpha} \propto \frac{z_1}{p\beta} \propto \frac{z_1\sqrt{1-\beta^2}}{M\beta^2}$$

Specific ionization or energy loss
$$I = z_1{}^2 f(\beta)$$

Residual range
$$R = \frac{M}{z_1{}^2} f_2(\beta)$$

Čerenkov angle
$$\psi_v = \cos^{-1}[1/n(v)\beta]$$

In general, the determination of velocity, charge and mass requires the measurement of three observable quantities. In some instances, however, one can draw conclusions from the value of a single one. Apart from the trivial case of the Čerenkov angle the most important example is the widely used selection of singly charged particles by measurements of ionization alone. This is made possible by the shape of the $I - p$ curve, which is such that a track with ionization below the minimum value of the curve for $z_1 = 2$ must be due to a singly charged particle.

Counters

During the past few years the subject of counter techniques has gradually grown so that it now forms one of the most important branches of experimental physics. This has been due in part to a great development of the electronic circuits with which counters are operated, and in part to the new types of counters which have come into use, among which the scintillation counter and Čerenkov counter should be particularly remarked. In the following discussion, however, it is only necessary to touch very briefly on these subjects, and we shall first consider the counting instrument which is still most widely used in the study of cosmic radiation. This detector, which is usually just called a counter, may be of the Geiger–Müller or of the proportional type, the difference lying mostly in the working conditions of the instrument. Such a counter is basically a sort of ionization chamber, i.e. a closed chamber with two electrodes, between which a current is induced by ionization.

In Fig. 4 is shown a schematic drawing of a counter. Along the axis of a thin metal tube is suspended a very thin wire, which is supported by insulators, so that the tube and the wire can act as the two electrodes. The tube, which is closed at both ends, is filled with a suitable gas, and the wire is kept at a positive potential with respect to the housing. Electrons, released by ionization in the chamber, will therefore be accelerated towards the axis and, in the strong field

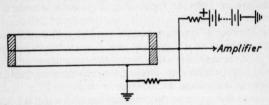

FIG. 4. Diagrammatic sketch of a counter

close to the thin wire, they may ionize and produce secondary electrons which are themselves accelerated by the stronger field. In this way each initial ion pair is primary to an electron avalanche, and a charged particle traversing the counter produces a current pulse, which by the multiplication effect may be sufficiently high to be detected above the background of amplifier noise. The instrument can thus detect single particles and is therefore operated with a circuit of relaxation time as short as possible.

The magnitude of the multiplication effect drops with decreasing potential on the wire, so that it is absent for very low voltages, where the counter acts as a badly designed ionization chamber. With increasing voltage the multiplication sets in, and in a certain region the current pulse is proportional to the number of primary ions produced. The proportionality holds until the avalanches initiated by the primary ions become so large that they seriously interfere with one another. In this potential region the instrument is said to work as a proportional counter. At a much higher voltage a continuous discharge sets in, but below this point there is a rather wide potential range—the Geiger region— where the pulse size is quite independent of the amount of ionization produced in the counter. The Geiger-counter, then, simply provides one pulse of sufficient size to be easily detected, for each particle which passes through it, perhaps best justifying the name 'counter'. As such it has the widest range of applications, particularly in conjunction with other counters or different types of particle detectors such as cloud chambers.

A number of counters may be used in conjunction with each other, so that a pulse is only recorded at the output stage of the amplifier when several fire 'simultaneously'; i.e. within a very short time-interval. The counters are then said to be in *coincidence*. An alternative condition of recording could be that some of the counters fire after a certain delay time (*delayed coincidence*), or that some of them do not fire at all (*anticoincidence*).

The simplest application of these principles is a row of counters in coincidence. Such a *counter telescope* defines a direction with any desired precision, and it can be used to measure angular distribution of intensity or to expand a cloud chamber immediately after it has been traversed by particles in a suitable direction (counter-controlled cloud chamber). Another useful property of the counter telescope is that it counts only charged particles, for, although a single counter may be fired by electrons released by a photon, the effectiveness in counting γ-rays is only about one per cent., and the simultaneous firing of several counters is therefore very improbable.

Still more information can be obtained from counter systems arranged in various patterns around absorbers. An example is shown in Fig. 5 of such a system which may be operated in several ways. Here the circles represent counters (as seen from the end) and the shaded blocks are absorbers.

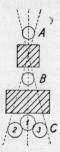

FIG. 5. A counter telescope *AB*, in conjunction with a third set of counters, *C*, which could be used to detect showers (*C* in coincidence with *AB*) or particles which stop in the absorber above *C* (*C* in anticoincidence with *AB*)

By counting fivefold coincidences between all the counters shown, events are selected, in which a particle, after penetrating the top absorber, produces a shower of secondaries in the second absorber. If, on the other hand, the counters 1, 2 and 3 are operated in anticoincidence with the coincidence system A–B, then particles are selected which penetrate the first absorber and are stopped—or heavily scattered—in the lower one.

Further examples of counter systems are discussed elsewhere in this book: e.g. a system for studying shower production (Fig. 2), a delayed coincidence system for lifetime measurements (Fig. 28), a magnetic analyser for selecting positive or negative particles (Fig. 29), and the magnetic hodoscope (Fig. 36).

Quite recently, counter systems have also been designed to measure the mass of the traversing particles. Using telescopes in connexion with a magnetic field, one may select

C

particles with magnetic rigidity within a certain interval, and the ionization of the particles is then measured in proportional counters in coincidence with the telescopes. If the particle is singly charged its mass can be estimated from the measured values of $H\rho$ and I. The precision of such measurements is, however, very much inferior to that of the best mass determinations made in cloud chambers or emulsions. The use of counters to provide in a short time information of good statistical weight on the intensity of specific components, the nature of which have been previously identified by other methods, remains their most important application.

Special counters must be designed for the detection of neutrons which do not ionize. Among these the most important is perhaps the boron counter, which is a proportional counter containing boron in form of a gas such as BF_3. Neutrons passing the counter may react with the boron in an (n, α) process, and the secondary α-particle together with the Li-recoil, which are both strongly ionizing, will then fire the proportional counter, even when its amplifier bias is set so that it does not detect fast singly charged particles. As the boron reaction has its largest cross-section for very slow neutrons, the effectiveness of the counter is increased by surrounding it by a thick layer of paraffin in which the neutrons are slowed down.

Finally we mention the Čerenkov counters, although they have not yet been much used in the study of cosmic radiation. The Čerenkov radiation given off, when a particle traverses a suitable radiator, may be collected by a system of mirrors and 'focused' on a photomultiplier tube, which detects photons very effectively. From the geometry of the mirrors one may calculate the approximate Čerenkov angle, ψ, and thus obtain an estimate of the particle velocity. Quite often, however, one is satisfied with a very rough definition of the angle, because even then the Čerenkov counter has the unique property of recording only the particles passing one way through the instrument. It is the only counter which can be used to select particles moving in a chosen direction; a counter telescope does not discriminate between particles moving upwards or downwards.

Cloud chambers

Although the fact that ionizing particles can produce tracks in photographic emulsions was discovered about the same time as C. T. R. Wilson operated his first cloud chamber (1912), it was not until after the second World War that the emulsion was sufficiently developed to become a major tool in cosmic ray or nuclear physics research. The slow development of the emulsion technique was largely due to the outstanding success achieved by the cloud chambers, especially as developed by Blackett and Occhialini (1933) for use with counter telescopes.

A cloud chamber is shown schematically in Fig. 6. In essence it consists of a closed vessel containing gas and vapour together with some free liquid, which is usually a water-alcohol mixture. The bottom of the chamber is a piston or other expansion device. In the steady state the gas in the chamber is just saturated with vapour, but as soon as the gas is suddenly expanded the temperature will drop, causing supersaturation of the vapour. Provided that the expansion time is short compared to the time necessary for heat transfer from the surroundings, the expansion will be approximately adiabatic, and the drop of temperature can be rather exactly controlled by altering the ratio of final volume to initial volume (volume-controlled chamber) or final pressure to initial pressure (pressure-controlled chamber).

If the degree of supersaturation is not too large the vapour will condense only on dust particles or ions present in the gas. Thus, in a clean chamber the column of ions produced by the passage of a charged particle may serve as nucleation centres for the condensation, and the track will appear as a row of droplets. When these have had sufficient time to grow the track is illuminated by a flash of light and photographed through the glass coverplate; a stereoscopic camera is used so that the position and shape of the track can be reconstructed. To be well focused the track must lie in a shallow region between the cover and the bottom of

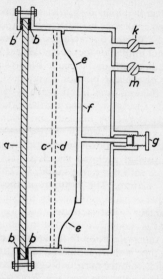

FIG. 6. Diagrammatic sketch of a cloud chamber. (*a*) Glass coverplate. (*b*) Rubber gaskets. (*c*) Piece of black velvet used to reduce gas turbulence and as photographic background. (*d*) Wire gauze. (*e*) Rubber membrane. (*f*) Piston. (*g*) Adjustable piston stop. (*k, m*) Valves to high- and low-pressure reservoirs

the chamber, and for the study of cosmic radiation cloud chambers are therefore set up with the coverplate in a vertical plane.

Many technical difficulties must be overcome and the chamber carefully adjusted if the photographs are to be useful for measurements on the tracks. During the expansion turbulent motions may be initiated which distort the track, and further distortion may arise from the convection currents involved in the reheating of the gas. The first source of distortion is counteracted by using a monoatomic gas which yields the necessary temperature drop with a small expansion ratio, and by placing a suitable velvet screen above the piston to damp the turbulence. The convection currents cannot be avoided, but the distortion is minimized if the photograph is taken very quickly after the expansion. This is also desirable in order to forestall the gravitational fall of the droplets. On the other hand, a lower limit to the time between the expansion and the photographing is set by the time required by the droplets to grow.

Another factor of importance, which affects the appearance of the track, is the time delay between the formation of the track and the expansion. The ions will diffuse away from their initial position, and an 'early' track will therefore be broad, with good resolution of the individual droplets, while a 'late' track, formed after the expansion, will be much narrower. Particles traversing the chamber more than a few seconds before the expansion do not produce tracks at all but tend to form a foggy background. To avoid the effect of such 'old tracks' one may apply an electrostatic cleaning field, which is switched off immediately before the expansion. This procedure is not possible in counter-controlled cloud chambers, but in the study of cosmic radiation, which has a low intensity, the problem of old tracks is rarely severe.

All these restrictions on the time delay between the track formation and the various operations of the chamber causes the sensitive time per expansion to be much less than one second, which is very little compared to the minimum delay between subsequent expansions. After an expansion the chamber must be cleared of drops and return to a state of temperature equilibrium and saturation, which involves a time of about a minute; a little less for small chambers and rather more for big chambers. Although, quite recently, the cycling time has been reduced by introducing an intermediate over-compression, the useful time of a cloud chamber is still a very small fraction of the actual working time. The invention of counter control was therefore of great importance to cosmic ray work.

In a counter-controlled cloud chamber the duration of the sensitive time is not so important since the expansions are not performed at random, but immediately after the passage of a particle. Using counter telescopes one can select flat tracks, which are suitable for measurement, and, by using more complicated counter systems, special events may be selected; e.g. showers, or particles decaying in the chamber. With such an experimental arrangement the average interval between expansions depends on the rarity of those events which can fire the chamber, provided that the chance of observing two of them within the recycling time of the chamber is small. Many fewer photographs are taken than with a chamber expanding at random, but one obtains more *useful* photographs per hour, and less time is wasted in scanning useless ones.

If the cloud chamber is placed in a magnetic field the magnetic rigidity of a particle can be determined by measuring the curvature of its track. The accuracy which can be obtained is restricted by the size of the chamber, the width of the track and by distortion in the gas. As a consequence the upper limit of measurable momenta is $p/z_1 \approx 10$ BeV.† In the low velocity region the major source of error is the multiple scattering in the gas, which increases as $1/v$ relative to the magnetic deflection. For intermediate momenta one can obtain very good determinations of p/z_1, and one must also remember the very important fact that the sign of the charge follows from the sense of the magnetic deflection.

Another observable quantity in the cloud chamber is the density of droplets in the track, which is a measure of the ionization produced by the particle. The drop density, how-

† 1 BeV. = 1 GeV. = 10^3 MeV.

ever, is very sensitive to small variations of the physical conditions in the chamber, and it is difficult to determine in an objective way. Only for weakly ionizing particles or for very broad tracks, where the individual droplets are well resolved, is it possible to perform a reliable counting; but unfortunately broad tracks are not suitable for measurements of curvature. The ionization is therefore not much used in the quantitative analysis of tracks in cloud chambers. Usually a rough visual estimate of the 'density' of a track is sufficient to distinguish between positrons and protons of moderate momenta, or to select fast particles of unit charge. Better estimates of the velocity may be obtained by measuring the energy loss of the particle when it traverses a lead plate or other absorber placed in the chamber. For a particle of given charge the energy loss depends only on the velocity, and the mass can therefore be deduced from measurements of curvature on both sides of the absorber plate. This method was used in the first observations of the positron and the μ-meson.

A closely related, and more accurate, procedure is to combine curvature measurements with measurements of the residual range, which is a very well defined and easily observable quantity. This kind of analysis was applied to the μ-meson shown on Plate III, and resulted in a very good mass determination. However, such events, where a particle stops in the gas, are extremely rare because of the small density of matter in the sensitive volume. Therefore, if range measurements are to be applied systematically, a number of thin absorber plates are set up in the chamber, so that the range can be estimated from the number of plates traversed by the particle before it is stopped. However, due to the multiple scattering in the plates and the distortion of the track, the magnetic rigidity cannot be measured in such *multiplate chambers*, and the range measurements must therefore be combined with some other observable quantity, which may be either the ionization or the multiple scattering in the plates. The first of these is difficult to measure with any precision, so that it gives only qualitative information on the particle, and the scattering is not much better. This is due to poor statistics in the determination of $\bar{\alpha}$ as an average of the deflections in the rather small number of plates traversed. Multiplate chambers are therefore not suitable for accurate mass determina-

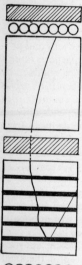

tions, but they have been used for the analysis of cascade showers and in the study of the decay products of unstable particles stopping in a plate. The fact that the multiplate chamber can detect photons by their interactions in the plates is an important feature in both types of experiment (see also Chapter 5).

Only recently (since 1952) techniques have been developed to combine precise measurements of curvature and range. The work was induced by the urgent need for good mass determinations on the heavy mesons, and the instrument invented was the *double cloud chamber*, which is shown schematically in Fig. 7. The curvature is measured in the top chamber, which is placed in a magnetic field, and the residual range is determined in the multiplate chamber below, which is fired at the same time as

Fig. 7. Double cloud chamber

the upper chamber by the same counter control system. The method has been very successful, yielding mass values with an error of only a few per cent. on a single measurement.

In addition to the ordinary cloud chamber we shall finally mention a few related instruments, which have not been widely used in cosmic ray work. The *high-pressure cloud chamber* contains gas at a pressure of 70–100 atmospheres. Thus, particles can be stopped more easily in the gas, but the corresponding increase of multiple scattering interferes with magnetic deflections without being sufficient to make $\bar{a}$ a good observable quantity. In the *diffusion chamber* the gas is not expanded, but vapour diffuses from the heated top to the cooled bottom of the chamber. In between, at a certain level, there is a stationary state of supersaturation, and in this permanently sensitive region tracks can be formed. The diffusion chamber can only be operated in a horizontal position. The *bubble chamber* contains a liquid, which in the steady state is compressed and at a temperature just below the boiling-point. After expansion boiling starts on ions in the liquid, and the track of a traversing particle may therefore appear as a row of bubbles. This instrument has many advantages; the filling can be a pure element such as liquid hydrogen, helium, argon or xenon, but the diffusion of the ions in the liquid is so fast that it has not been possible to construct counter-controlled bubble chambers.

Nuclear emulsions

An ionizing particle, traversing a photographic emulsion, can act on the silver halide grains which it penetrates along its trajectory in such a way that some of them are rendered developable. Thus, after processing, the track will be observed as a row of silver grains in the gelatine, provided that the sensitivity of the emulsion is sufficiently high. Ordinary photographic plates fulfil this condition for very strongly ionizing particles, and, as mentioned above, the idea of detecting particles with emulsions is as old as the cloud chamber. But it was not until very recently that emulsions were developed into the precise measuring medium which is now known by the name nuclear emulsion. This was achieved by increasing the concentration of silver halide by a factor of eight, and by a programme of research which has revealed methods of increasing the sensitivity of the individual grains, so that in modern emulsion tracks can be produced even by singly charged particles of minimum ionization (electron sensitive emulsions).

The composition of a typical emulsion is set out in Table 2.1.

TABLE 2.1

COMPOSITION OF ILFORD EMULSIONS

Element	Z	g./cm.^{3}	Atoms/cm.^{3} ($\times 10^{22}$)
I	53	0·052	0·02
Ag	47	1·85	1·04
Br	35	1·34	1·02
S	16	0·010	0·02
O	8	0·27	1·01
N	7	0·067	0·29
C	6	0·27	1·36
H	1	0·056	3·35

Density 3·92 g./cm.^{3}

It should be remembered, however, that the figures given here are only valid for an emulsion surrounded by very dry air. With increasing humidity the gelatine absorbs water, so that, for the stacks actually used, the density reported is frequently 3·81–3·85. The relative composition is also changed slightly by the added water. It can be seen from the table that about 50 per cent. by volume, or 80 per cent. by weight, of the emulsion is composed of silver halide, and that the remaining portion contains negligibly few atoms of atomic number greater than eight. The large amount of silver halide which must be removed in the fixing process causes the emulsion layer to shrink, so that its thickness after processing is approximately halved. The shrinking is usually accompanied by lateral distortions of the emulsion layer, and great care must be taken to keep this effect to a minimum. Other problems are to obtain a suitable degree of development without too many background grains, and to avoid large gradients in the development as a function of depth in the emulsion.

In the practical analysis of particle tracks it is frequently important to be able to make the measurements on very long sections of track, or to trace the track of a particle to the end of its range. Consequently there has been a tendency towards the use of thicker emulsion layers. However, the difficulties of processing increase very rapidly with increasing emulsion thickness, and in practice layers of more than 2 mm. have not been used. It was therefore a tremendous step forward when *stripped emulsions* came into general use in 1953. The individual emulsion sheets, which, after pouring, have been stripped from their glass backings, can be stacked together to form a large, continuous, sensitive volume. After exposure, the emulsion sheets can be re-mounted on glass plates and processed in the usual way. The relative position of the emulsions at exposure can be reconstructed from reference marks made with a narrow X-ray pencil on the edges of the sheets in the stack, and a more accurate adjustment can be obtained by means of steep tracks of heavily ionizing particles. After making such an adjustment it is possible to trace the track of a particle through the whole stack, and one has thus obtained, effectively, a large block of emulsion without the difficulties of processing and observation associated with the use of glass plates with thick emulsion layers. As an illustration of the great possibilities of the new method it may be mentioned that stacks containing more than 200 stripped emulsion sheets, each of size 25 cm. × 35 cm. × 0·6 mm., have been exposed. In such stacks it was possible to obtain much new information on the secondary particles from the decay of heavy mesons, because the charged secondaries could often be traced to the end of their range (more than 20 cm.) and thus be identified by their mode of decay.

Nuclear emulsions, particularly in the stripped form, are very well adapted to work in the cosmic ray field, for they are simple and robust, and they can easily be exposed at very great altitudes in the atmosphere. While the heavy and complicated cloud chamber arrangements are difficult to operate at altitudes greater than those of mountain-peaks, emulsion stacks can be carried by free balloons, and in this way they are frequently exposed for several hours at altitudes of 20-30 km., returning to earth, after a predetermined exposure, by parachute.

From the point of view of track analysis, the major differences between cloud chambers and emulsions are due to the widely different densities of matter in the sensitive volume. Thus, the volume of a cloud chamber, designed to stop high energy particles as efficiently as one of the large emulsion stacks, would have to be of the order of 1 cu. km. In the emulsion the length of tracks is, so to speak, scaled down by the large density, and the same is true for the width of the tracks, the diameter of the silver grains being only about half a micron. For this reason the processed emulsion must be scanned, and the tracks measured, under the microscope. Although this is very time-consuming, it has the advantage that fine details of the tracks can be observed, and emulsions are therefore well suited to the study of unstable particles of very short lifetime (π^0-mesons, hyperfragments), for which the spatial separation of production and decay may be considerably less than the diameter of a single droplet in a cloud chamber. However, for neutral particles, which traverse macroscopic distances between production and decay or interaction, the cloud chamber is superior, because the appearance of the related events on the same photograph greatly facilitates the observation and the proof of correlation. For this reason the cloud chamber has been the major tool in the study of neutral hyperons and in the search for γ-rays among decay products of unstable particles. Details of nuclear disintegrations produced by fast particles, or of the decay at rest of charged mesons, can best be investigated with emulsions, because in a cloud chamber such processes will nearly always occur in an absorber plate, i.e. outside the sensitive volume.

The relative merit of the various measurable track parameters is also strongly affected by the high density of the emulsion. Magnetic rigidity, the quantity which can be most accurately measured in the cloud chamber, is useless in the emulsion, because the high concentration of heavy atoms results in a strong multiple scattering. For this very reason, however, the scattering parameter, $\bar{\alpha}$, can be rather accurately measured in emulsions. The usual definition of the scattering constant is based on a subdivision of the track into 100 μ cells, and $\bar{\alpha}_{100}$ is then defined as the numerical arithmetic mean of the angles between subsequent chords to the plane projection of the track. Single scatters are usually eliminated by omitting angles greater than four times the mean value. The scattering constant is then, to a good approximation, $C \approx 25$ degrees $\times$ MeV., so that $\bar{\alpha}_{100} \approx 25\, z_1/pv$ degrees, where pv is measured in MeV.

The observation of very small deflections can be affected by imperfections in the motion of the microscope stage, but with suitable design the decisive factor becomes the finite grain size, which is such that the track position can only be defined to within $\approx 0\cdot 1$ μ. The contributions to the observed scattering from these sources of error are called 'stage noise' and 'grain noise' respectively. For very energetic particles it is necessary to use cells of a larger size, $\Delta \gg 100$ μ, in order to obtain an average deflection, $\bar{\alpha}_\Delta \approx \bar{\alpha}_{100}(\Delta/100\ \mu)^{1/2}$, which is sufficiently above the noise-level. In large cells, however, the measured deflections can be affected by distortions of the emulsion, and in practice values of pv/z_1 greater than ≈ 10 BeV. cannot be measured with much accuracy. For low energy particles it is sometimes advantageous to use cells considerably shorter than 100 μ, for the number of cells in a given track should always be as large as possible to secure good statistics in the determination of $\bar{\alpha}$. The choice of cell length, for any given track, is therefore a compromise between the short cells which provide good statistics and the long cells which render the effect of noise negligible. For long tracks, which may be divided into several hundred cells, it is possible to obtain estimates of pv/z_1 with a statistical error of less than 5 per cent., but distortions may render the result subject to systematic errors which are difficult to estimate.

Much higher accuracy can be obtained in measurements of the ionization, I. For very 'thin' tracks, due to fast singly charged particles, a suitable measure of I is the grain density, g, which is determined simply by counting the number of grains per unit length of track. It is true that the absolute value of g depends on the degree of development, but neighbouring tracks of very fast particles ($\gamma > 20$; tracks from high energy electron pairs are often used) can be used to calibrate the emulsion, for such particles ionize at the 'plateau' level, so that the corresponding grain density, g_{pl}, is a measure of the degree of development of the emulsion. The 'normalized grain density', $g^* = g/g_{pl}$, has been found to depend very little on development, and this quantity is therefore a convenient measure of I.

Slow particles, or particles of higher charge, produce denser tracks, where many grains overlap to form columns of silver, so that the tracks will appear more or less 'grey' or even 'black'. It is then difficult to count the individual grains, but for grey tracks one can still estimate I by counting the number of columns per unit path (blob density). In black tracks one concentrates instead on the gaps between the columns, and it has been shown that the reciprocal mean gap length is a useful estimate of I. Methods have recently been developed for measuring mean gap length with high precision, so that for long tracks the statistical error can be about 1 per cent., including the uncertainty of calibration measurements on neighbouring tracks of known velocity.

Tracks produced by very strongly ionizing particles show very few gaps, and the ionization must therefore be estimated from the density of δ-rays which exceed some convenient energy limit. In practice, such δ-rays are selected by counting only secondary tracks containing more than a certain number of grains. Scattering measurements may be used to select particles which are sufficiently energetic to lie on the ionization plateau, and for such particles the δ-ray density is directly proportional to z_1^2. Their charge can therefore be determined by comparison with calibration α-particles. A method of this kind was used to measure the charge spectrum of the primary particles in the cosmic radiation (Fig. 13). The appearance of tracks produced by fast particles of various charges is shown in Fig. 8.

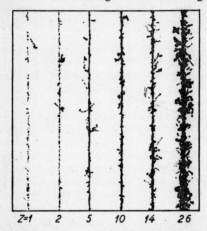

FIG. 8. The appearance in the photographic emulsion of the tracks of relativistic particles of various charges

For singly charged particles combined measurements of $\bar{a}$ and I can be used to obtain rough mass estimates. The principle of the method is illustrated in Fig. 9, in which $g^* = g/g_{pl}$ is plotted as a function of $p\beta = pv/c$. It will be noticed that π-mesons, K-mesons, protons and deuterons are well resolved, provided that their ionization is sufficiently above the plateau value. Really accurate mass measurements can, however, only be made on particles which come

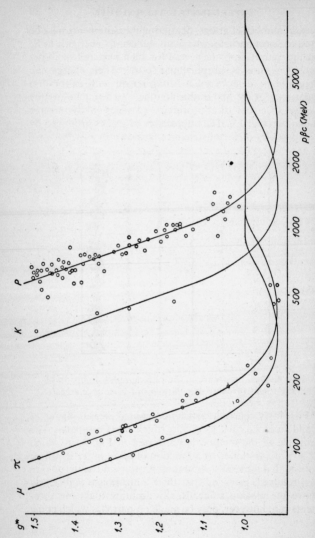

Fig. 9. The determination of the mass of singly charged particles by scattering (pβc) *vs.* grain

to rest in the emulsion, because only for these can one obtain additional information by measuring the well-defined quantity R, the residual range. One rapid experimental method is based on the combination of measurements of $\bar{a}$ and R, but due to the limited accuracy in the determination of $\bar{a}$, the resulting mass values are not very reliable. A much better procedure is to measure I as a function of R, using similar measurements on the track of an identified particle in the same region of the emulsion for calibration. The mass determination can then be based on the exact relation (2.6) which states that singly charged particles of the same velocity, and hence producing tracks of the same grain density, have residual ranges proportional to their rest masses. The resulting mass values can be correct to within a few per cent. for measurements on a long track.

D

CHAPTER 3

The Primary Radiation

Entering the top of the earth's atmosphere there is a continuous stream of high energy particles which produce the complicated chain of events associated with the secondary cosmic radiation observed in the atmosphere. The total energy brought in by these primary particles is of the same order of magnitude as that of starlight. A detailed study of the primary radiation, though difficult, is of considerable importance, both from the point of view of being able to use the cosmic radiation as a source of very high energy particles for the study of nuclear physics, and from that of trying to solve the problem of the production of the radiation and the means by which such colossal energies are given to individual particles.

Geomagnetic effects

That the primary radiation must contain a large proportion of charged particles has long been known from the occurrence of variations in the mean intensity of the radiation which can be correlated with the geomagnetic latitude, longitude, and the direction of observation. The most important of these are the dependence of the intensity on the geomagnetic latitude of observation, the latitude effect, and the east–west effect, which is the asymmetry of the intensities from the westerly and easterly directions at a given point of observation.

The theory of these effects is based on a study of the possible trajectories of singly charged particles in the magnetic field of the earth, which is usually approximated by a simple dipole field. At any given point on the surface of the earth, a particle can, of course, move in any direction, irrespective of the magnitude of its momentum. But this trivial fact does not imply that all these possible trajectory segments can be traversed by cosmic ray particles. When the complete trajectories, corresponding to each segment and all values of the particle momentum, are considered, it is found that some of them are bound in the earth's magnetic field in such a way that they are inaccessible to particles starting at infinite distances from the earth. In other instances, although the trajectory may be traced back to infinity, it is found that it has already passed through the volume of the solid earth before reaching the point of observation. The corresponding direction of observation is then said to lie within the earth's shadow. An extremely simple example is provided by particles of very low momentum. The trajectories of such particles are helices about the magnetic field lines, and it is easily seen that they can only carry such cosmic ray particles as arrive at the poles.

If we consider a given point on the surface of the earth, and some given momentum, cosmic ray particles can only be observed in certain directions, which are therefore called 'allowed directions', while all other directions are forbidden. A detailed discussion of the cones of allowed directions is beyond the scope of this book. The cones have a complicated structure and they are determined by making numerical calculations on large numbers of trajectories. It is, however, not necessary to calculate trajectories for every possible momentum and direction, as it is possible to find certain classes of trajectories which limit rather simple cones which can be shown to contain only allowed or forbidden directions.

Before going on to a more detailed discussion of the allowed cones, we shall, as an illustration to the above discussion, consider the simple problem of charged particles moving in the equatorial plane of the earth. Under these conditions it is particularly easy to see how a direction can be classified as forbidden or allowed.

Consider a particle moving in the earth's equatorial plane (Fig. 10). As the total energy of the particle is not altered by the magnetic field, the radius of curvature of its path as a function of the distance, r, from the centre of the earth, will be proportional to the inverse of the magnetic field strength, and hence to r^3. The path of a

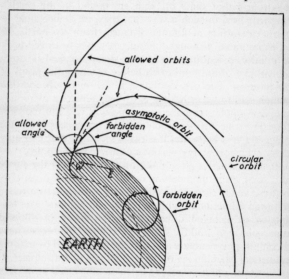

FIG. 10. The motion of positively charged particles in the equatorial plane of the earth

particle which arrives at some given point with a momentum, p, and a direction, ϕ, measured from the eastern horizon, will be the same as that of a particle of opposite sign ejected from the earth's surface along the same line of motion, and with the same momentum.

When the momentum, p, is small, a negative particle sent off with a direction which lies close to the eastern horizon, so that ϕ is small, will be bent back towards the earth again so that (neglecting the fact that the earth is solid) it will remain in a bound orbit which always stays close to the earth. Such a particle cannot reach infinity, and therefore no cosmic ray particles of the value of p considered can reach the earth in the chosen direction. As the angle of emission, ϕ, is increased, the maximum distance from the centre of the earth, which the particle reaches before it is bent back again, increases, until, for a certain value of $\phi = \phi_1$, which depends on p, the path approaches asymptotically a circular orbit which is concentric with the earth, and whose radius, r', is related to the momentum of the particle and the dipole moment of the magnetic field of the earth by the relation:

$$p = (eM/c)/r'^2, \qquad (3.1)$$

where M is the dipole moment of the earth. It may be shown that the circular orbit can be approached by a particle of momentum p either from the inside, as discussed above, or from the outside.

If the angle of emission is increased still further, beyond ϕ_1, then the particle will be able to cross the circular orbit and escape to infinity. Thus *positive* particles with momentum p can only approach the earth in its equatorial plane at angles greater than ϕ_1. If the approaching particles had been negatively charged, the only difference would be that the angle ϕ would have had to be measured from the western horizon.

For a given value of p, all orbits which reach the surface of the earth with an angle $< \phi_1$ are bounded, and, as seen above, no cosmic ray primaries can arrive from this portion of the sky, but for $\phi > \phi_1$ all directions are allowed, for the orbits are unbounded. Equation (3.1) allows one to calculate roughly the smallest momentum at which all directions of approach are allowed, for the condition that the primaries can reach the earth horizontally from the eastern direction corresponds to the condition that the radius of the earth is equal to the radius of the circular orbit discussed above. Thus we have:

$$P = \left(\frac{eM}{c}\right) \Big/ R_E{}^2 = 59,300 \text{ MeV.}/c, \qquad (3.2)$$

where R_E is the radius of the earth. In general, if one considers other momenta, the curvature of the paths drawn in Fig. 10 will be altered, but it may be shown that this can be considered to be merely a matter of scale. It is easily seen from equation (3.1) that the earth's radius should be drawn proportional to $p^{1/2}$. Thus, the dotted circle on the diagram represents the choice of a smaller momentum which is such that particles can reach the surface of the earth only from the western horizon. No particles of smaller momentum can reach the earth's surface.

For a given momentum, p, it may be shown that the minimum angle, ϕ_1, with which a particle can reach the earth's surface is given by the relation:

$$\cos \phi_1 = 2\sqrt{\frac{P}{p}} - \frac{P}{p}. \qquad (3.3)$$

When latitudes and directions other than the equator and the equatorial plane are considered, it is found that, to a first approximation, the allowed directions lie within a cone, the axis of which lies in the east–west direction and whose half-angle $(\pi - \phi_1)$ may be found from the equation:

$$p = P\frac{\cos^4 \lambda}{\{(g_c{}^2 - \cos \phi_1 \cos^3 \lambda)^{1/2} + g_c\}^2}, \qquad (3.4)$$

where λ is the geomagnetic latitude, and g_c is a constant whose value is close to unity and depends on the latitude. The cone found by putting $g_c = 1$ is known as the Störmer cone, and for many purposes it is a sufficient approximation. It must be remarked, however, that the above results for the simple Störmer cone do not take into account the effects due to a *solid* earth. These effects are complex and will not be discussed in detail here.

The derivation of the intensity of particles of some given

momentum inside the allowed cone is based upon the assumption that the radiation at great distances from the earth is isotropic, and on the use of Liouville's theorem. In this context this states that a group of particles starting from a given volume element, δV, with a given range of momenta, $p \rightarrow p + \delta p$, will produce a beam of constant intensity along their path. Thus, if a direction of approach is allowed for particles of some given momentum, and if the intensity of the radiation is isotropic at great distances from the earth, then the intensity of such particles reaching the surface of the earth is the same as that at great distances from the earth.

The above relationships between the momenta and the allowed angles are the results of an approximate treatment by Störmer in 1934, and do not take into account the fact of a *solid* earth. The simplest effect of the solid earth is, of course, the removal from the allowed cone of those directions which lie below the horizon. While a more detailed treatment by Lemaître and Vallarta, based on the numerical calculation of orbits, confirms that no trajectories not allowed by the Störmer treatment reach the earth, it also shows that not all directions within the Störmer cone are allowed. First, there are certain directions within the Störmer cone which, even when the solidity of the earth is not taken into account, can be shown to be forbidden. Second, there are certain trajectories within the Störmer cone which are such that they have already intersected the earth's surface one or more times (Fig. 11). As the particles in question are stopped when they first meet the earth, these directions will lie within the shadow of the earth. This shadow is concentrated around the direction of the nearer pole, where there is a region of complete darkness. Between the regions of complete darkness and that of complete light, called the main cone (*not* a circular cone), there exists a region where there are many alternating bands of light and darkness. This region is called the penumbrum and is most extensive at intermediate latitudes.

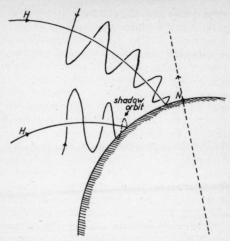

FIG. 11. The origin of the shadow cone

The latitude effect

From equation (3.4) it is clear that the minimum allowed momentum in any direction decreases as the latitude increases. Thus, at low latitudes, near the equator, all that part of the primary radiation of energy less than 10 BeV. fails to reach the top of the atmosphere, so that the total intensity of the radiation observed at the equator is smaller than that observed at higher latitudes. On the other hand, particles which reach sea-level at higher latitudes cannot have been produced by very low energy primaries, for they could not then have acquired sufficient energy to penetrate the atmosphere, and, in fact, it is found that at sea-level there is no appreciable change in the intensity with increasing latitude for $\lambda > 45°$. The magnitude of the latitude effect at sea-level is about 14 per cent. From this one may conclude that only 14 per cent. of the particles which penetrate to sea-level are secondary to primary particles

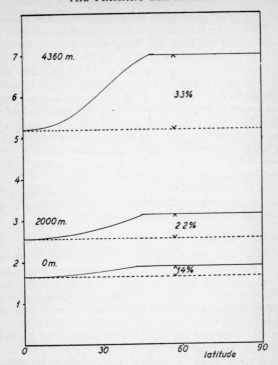

FIG. 12. The latitude effect at three different altitudes.
(Based on the data of Compton, *Phys. Rev.*, **43**, 387
(1933))

of energy less than 15 BeV. (here we use, of course, the
vertical intensity, for the intensity at large angles to the
vertical is attenuated by a very much thicker layer of
atmosphere).

At greater altitudes, the latitude effect is more marked,
for here secondaries to lower energy primaries play a much

more important part. From the relations discussed above, the 'knee' of the latitude curve, which we have seen occurs at $\lambda = 45°$ at sea-level, will be expected to move further from the equator, so that, above the atmosphere, it will have completely disappeared. At very high altitudes, the experimental results with respect to the existence or non-existence of the 'knee' are contradictory. If it does exist, then it must be interpreted as meaning that there is a lower energy limit in the spectrum of the primary cosmic radiation. It has recently been suggested that some of the contradictory experimental results can be explained if the 'knee' is not constant, but shifts from time to time, being absent when there is a sunspot minimum.

Fig. 12 shows the latitude effect at a number of different altitudes, the data from which the curves are calculated being that of Compton and his co-workers.

The east-west effect

We have seen above that for positive particles of some given momentum parts of the eastern sky constitute forbidden directions. When the whole energy spectrum of the primary radiation is taken into account it is clear that, for positive primaries, there will be an excess of intensity from westerly directions over that from the corresponding easterly directions. All experimental evidence so far obtained on this point has suggested that the primary radiation is predominantly positively charged, for effects of the right order of magnitude have been observed by many workers. An unambiguous result on the charge of the primary radiation is, however, difficult to obtain, for this can only be supplied by measurements made above the atmosphere. Measurements made under greater or smaller thicknesses of atmosphere include the effects of many secondary particles, which to some extent will deviate in direction from the primary particles which created them, so smearing out the results. In view of the short time which a rocket spends above the atmosphere, and of the difficulty of orientating it, it has not been possible to obtain better information by their use.

The longitude effect

The magnetic centre of the earth does not coincide with the true centre, being displaced about 300 km. along the radius which intercepts the surface of the earth at 6·5° N. and 161·8° E., near the Philippines. Hence, there is an intensity variation along a line of constant geomagnetic latitude, the minimum occurring in the western Pacific and the maximum in the Atlantic Ocean. The magnitude of the effect along the geomagnetic equator is about 4 per cent.

The north-south effect

One of the results of the shadow effect discussed above is that there is a slight excess of radiation from the south in the northern hemisphere, and from the north in the southern hemisphere. The effect is expected to be at a maximum at intermediate latitudes, and measurements made by Johnson in Mexico in 1935 have given qualitative agreement with the theory. More recent measurements at the equator have failed, as expected from the theory, to show an effect.

The nature of the primary radiation

Of the various known types of particles, or agglomerates of particles, only nuclei, protons, photons and electrons could be primary cosmic radiation. Apart from failing to provide the geomagnetic effects, the secondaries to a beam of neutrinos would show no apparent absorption in the atmosphere. Mesons and neutrons are unstable, and would decay before they reached the earth. Electrons and photons have been ruled out as possibilities by some experiments due to Critchfield and his collaborators in 1950. A cloud chamber was flown at an altitude of about 28 km., well above the maximum of the altitude-intensity curve. The chamber was crossed by a number of absorbers, so that any electrons or photons entering it would cause the formation of easily detected electromagnetic cascades in the absorbing plates. From the results of these experiments they were able to conclude that, neglecting the effects of the production of the soft component in the atmosphere, electrons and photons constituted not more than 0·6 per cent. of the total flux of the primary radiation. When account was taken of the production of these particles in the upper atmosphere as secondaries to nuclear processes, it was possible to reduce the upper limit to 0·25 per cent.

As a result of the above considerations we can conclude that only protons and the stable nuclei of the elements could constitute the primary cosmic radiation. In the extreme relativistic range of velocities, within which the primary radiation enters the atmosphere, it is not possible to measure directly the masses of particles passing through, or causing interactions in, nuclear emulsions or counters, but, within certain limits, it is possible to determine their energies and charges. In this way it has been found that a very large proportion of the radiation measured at very high altitudes consists of singly charged particles. When emulsions are used, many of these particles are seen to cause interactions. These particles must be assumed to be protons.

In addition to the tracks of relativistic singly charged particles, emulsions flown at high altitudes also contain the tracks of multiply charged particles, which are now known to be the nuclei of the various elements from helium ($Z = 2$) to iron ($Z = 26$). These fragments have energies very much in excess of evaporation fragments from nuclear disintegrations, and therefore they must also be assigned to the primary cosmic radiation. That these nuclei must be stripped of their orbital electrons during the acceleration process is clear, and that they are still stripped when they enter the atmosphere may be deduced from observations on their latitude effect at very high altitudes. Again, if the particles possessed their orbital electrons before they en-

tered the atmosphere, they would lose them entirely before
they had traversed more than 1 gm./cm.² of air. Many of
these electrons would have considerable energies, for their
velocities would be the same as those of the primary nuclei,
and they would be expected to produce a soft component
whose intensity was about 2 per cent. of that of the total
radiation. We have seen above that this is not in accord
with the experimental facts.

The charge spectrum

The distribution in charge of the heavy, or multiply charged,
primary component of the cosmic radiation may be measured directly for elements above helium by exposing emulsions to the radiation, and then estimating the charge, by
δ-ray counting, of all the fast multiple charged particles
which traverse the plates. As it is not possible to reach the
very top of the atmosphere with nuclear emulsions, a correction must be applied to the results to take into account
the fact that some of the nuclei may have struck an air
nucleus before entering the plates, and have been broken
down into one or more fragments of smaller charge. The
effect is accentuated by the fact that the cross-section for
interaction increases with the mass of the incoming nucleus.
At a given depth in the atmosphere one therefore measures
too few highly charged particles, and, comparatively, too
many particles of small charge. The extent to which the
collisions of such heavy nuclei are important has been
estimated from a study of the variation of the relative
intensities as a function of the zenith angle, for particles
whose trajectories diverge from the vertical must have
traversed a considerably greater thickness of atmosphere
before reaching the plates.

Measurements on the charge spectrum of the primary
radiation have been made by a number of different groups,
and that obtained by Dainton and his collaborators in
Bristol is shown in Fig. 13. In this figure the α-particle
peak is not a measure of the relative intensity, the results

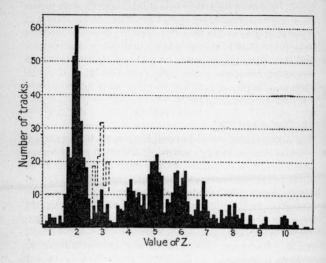

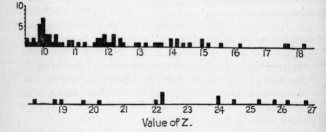

Fig. 13. Observed charge distribution of the primary radiation for $Z > 2$. (After Dainton *et al.*, *Phil. Mag.*, **43**, 749 (1952))

being valid only for particles of charge $Z > 2$. The α-particles are included for charge calibration. The dotted line represents the spectrum after a correction has been made for the loss of lithium tracks in scanning, but no correction has been made for the amount of matter passed through before the particles reached the plates. When such a correction is made, it is found that the number of lithium particles is about half that of the beryllium and boron, and that the beryllium and boron peaks together contain about the same number of particles as do the combined peaks due to carbon, nitrogen and oxygen. In general, the intensities decrease with increasing charge, and no certain examples of nuclei with charge greater than 26 have hitherto been observed. Another interesting feature of the spectrum is that nuclei of even charge are approximately three times as numerous as those of odd charge. It has been suggested that this is a result of the fact that the evenly charged nuclei have a larger number of stable isotopes. If the nuclei are produced as a monotonic function of mass, then the resulting β-decays of the unstable nuclei will produce just such a charge distribution. A mass distribution of the above type might be expected if the majority of the primary nuclei were secondary particles from nuclear interactions in interstellar space.

A number of other groups have also measured the charge spectrum of the primary radiation, and, with the exception of one very important point, the results are in general agreement with those quoted above. Thus, for example, Peters and his group, in a series of experiments, have found a charge spectrum which is similar to that shown in Fig. 13, apart from the absence of the peaks due to the elements lithium, beryllium and boron. On the other hand, Noon and his collaborators have recently made a new determination of the flux of these three elements under very favourable experimental conditions. They confirm the Bristol results.

When the charge distribution of the cosmic radiation is

compared with the abundances of the elements in the Universe, as determined by the astronomers, some degree of similarity is found. This may be seen in Table 3.1. Here it is seen that the universal abundance of lithium, beryllium and boron is zero. If one accepts the similarity at its face value, and assumes that the cosmic radiation is produced with a charge distribution which is exactly the same as that in the universe, then one may say that these light elements must have been produced by the break-up of heavier nuclei on their journey through interstellar space. In other words, the intensity of the lithium-beryllium-boron component might be used as a measure of the distance travelled by the radiation before it reaches the earth.

The existence of the lithium, beryllium and boron nuclei among the cosmic ray primaries is one difference between the abundances in the radiation and the universe. A more detailed study of Table 3.1 shows that the abundances of nuclei of $Z \geqslant 10$ are all greater than those observed in the universe. The recent measurements by Noon and his collaborators tend to emphasize this point. While the existence

TABLE 3.1

Element	Atomic Number Z	Abundance In the C.R.	Universe
H	1	100,000	100,000
He	2	10,000	10,000
Li	3⎫		
Be	4⎬	500	0
B	5⎭		
C	6⎫		
N	7⎬	520	130
O	8⎭		
Ne	10	30	2·6–70
Mg	12	40	2·5
Si	14	30	2·9
Fe	26	30	5
Others $Z \leqslant 30$		30	2·7
Others $Z > 30$		1	4×10^{-3}

of too many light nuclei can easily be explained in terms of the break-up of heavier nuclei, an excess of heavy nuclei would suggest the necessity of reconsidering our fundamental ideas on the origin of the primary radiation.

The energy spectrum of the primary radiation

In the lower energy region, up to about 10 BeV. per nucleon, the energy of the primary particles may be measured directly by scattering measurements in nuclear emulsions exposed at great altitudes, but at higher energies such direct methods are not practicable, and other methods must be used. Up to 15 BeV. per nucleon the geomagnetic latitude effect may be used to determine the energy spectra of the various types of primary particles, while at higher energies one must make use of the reactions produced by the primary particles in the atmosphere or in nuclear emulsions. One can, for example, measure the frequency and size distribution of extensive air showers (Chapter 8) at various levels in the atmosphere, and, although the relationship between the size of such showers and the energy of the primary particle that initiated them is not very well known, one may hope to learn something from the data of the slope of the spectrum at very high energies. Similarly, one may obtain indirect data from the energy spectrum of the very fast μ-mesons at sea-level and underground. More direct information may be had from studies of the nuclear interactions caused by high energy primaries in nuclear emulsions exposed at great altitudes. The method is not particularly reliable for protons, as the detailed processes which take place within a nucleus when a proton strikes it are not particularly well understood. The problem is simplest when the struck nucleus is itself a proton, for then the half-angle of the resulting shower of relativistic particles gives a measure of the energy of the primary particle. When the target nucleus is heavier, the secondary processes which take place within it will tend to increase the angular

E

divergence of the shower, and thus decrease the estimate of the primary energy made in this way.

When the primary is itself a heavier nucleus, the problem is simpler, for it is well known that the evaporation fragments of a struck nucleus are distributed isotropically with respect to the direction of motion of the incoming nucleus, and are emitted with energies which are not usually greater than a few MeV. Thus, the evaporation fragments of a nucleus, which is travelling very fast in the laboratory system of coordinates when it interacts, will form a narrow shower of protons and α-particles in addition to the shower of mesons normally created in high energy collisions. The evaporation protons and other fragments of the incoming nucleus will have velocities closely equal to that of the primary particle, and by studying the angular divergence of those particles with $Z \geqslant 2$, one may obtain a reasonably accurate estimate of the energy of the primary particle.

Peters has collected the available data on the energy spectra of the various components of the primary radiation and quotes the following relations for the integral spectra. The number of particles $N(E)$, M.$^{-2}$sec.$^{-1}$sterad.$^{-1}$, with kinetic energy greater than E (BeV.) is given by:

$$N(E) = K/(1 + E)^{1\cdot2} \dagger$$

for nuclei with $Z \geqslant 2$, while for protons the corresponding spectrum is given by:

$$N(E) = K/(1 + E).$$

The value of the constant K depends on the type of nucleus being considered, some values being set out in Table 3.2.

TABLE 3.2

Nucleus	Proton	He	Li, Be, B	C, N, O	$Z \geqslant 9$
K	3,800	380	19	20	6

$\dagger$ Recent experiments lead to an exponent $- 1\cdot5$ for the heavy particle spectra, and there is evidence that the proton spectrum should also have an exponent near $- 1\cdot5$, at least for energies > 100 BeV.

The intensity of the primary radiation

The best data on the total flux of charged particles entering the atmosphere have been obtained from rocket flights up to 150 km. altitude. The rockets are usually equipped with either a single counter, which measures the omni-directional intensity, or with a vertical counter which measures just the vertical intensity. A typical altitude-intensity curve from such a flight is shown in Fig. 14. Above the earth's

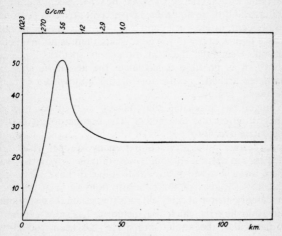

FIG. 14. Typical altitude-intensity curve obtained from a rocket flight. (After Gangnes *et al.*, *Phys. Rev.*, **75**, 57 (1949))

atmosphere the intensity is a constant as a function of altitude, but once the atmosphere is entered it rises to a sharp peak as the energy of the primary particles is shared among a number of charged and neutral secondaries. As these secondaries are absorbed by greater thicknesses of air, the measured intensity begins to fall off again rapidly, until, at sea-level, that remaining is a very small fraction of the initial primary intensity.

Taking the available data into account, one arrives at the following estimates for the intensity of the primary radiation. The number of particles arriving at the top of the atmosphere is about 3,000 M.$^{-2}$sec.$^{-1}$sterad.$^{-1}$ More detailed information is available for the latitude-sensitive range of energies. There are incident 3,600 nucleons M.$^{-2}$sec.$^{-1}$sterad.$^{-1}$ with energies between 0·35 and 8 BeV., carrying a total energy of 8,000 BeV.M.$^{-2}$sec.$^{-1}$sterad.$^{-1}$ (13 ergs). Of these nucleons, 66 per cent. arrive as protons, 26 per cent. in He nuclei and 8 per cent. in heavier nuclei. These figures apply to a region where there is no magnetic cut-off. Using the data on the energy spectra discussed above, it is possible to calculate the actual number of particles arriving at the top of the atmosphere at any particular latitude.

Singer has suggested that meteorites may be used as integrating cosmic ray meters. The bombardment of the meteorite over long periods of time in its journey through space results in the production of many isotopes which are very rare in nature. Although most of these are short-lived, there are a few which are either stable or have very long half-lives. Studies of the concentrations of such isotopes in meteoric material can yield information on the integrated radiation flux to which the meteorite has been exposed. In particular, the stable isotope He^3 has been studied by Paneth in this connexion, and certain studies have been made on the production of H^3 (half-life $\approx$ 12 years) in newly fallen meteorites. More recently the possibilities of using other long-lived isotopes which should be produced in small quantities, such as Mn^{53} (half-life 1–20 $\times$ 10^6 years), Be^{10} (half-life $\approx$ 10^6 years), and Al^{26} (half-life $\sim$ 10^5 years), have been discussed, but there are as yet no practical results. It is tempting to consider these meteors as a source of information about the very low energy end of the primary spectrum, but their large stopping power for charged particles, and the ablation of their outer skin during their fall through the atmosphere, limit their usefulness in this direction.

Intending space travellers can note with satisfaction that the intensity of the radiation is such that, even if the walls of the ship contain just sufficient matter to ensure that the radiation intensity in the cabin is a maximum, the total dosage rate to which they will be exposed is only about half the safety limit, at present accepted by most countries, for doses of long duration.

The origin of the primary radiation

Of the few experimental data which are of help in forming a theory of the origin of the primary radiation is the correlation between certain solar phenomena and the intensity of the radiation. There now exists evidence on variations of period 1 day and 27 days (the solar rotation period), as well as well-established correlations with the intensity of sunspots and solar flares. The total magnitude of the periodic effects is very small, being about 0·2 per cent. for the diurnal effect and about 1–2 per cent. for the 27-day effect. The variations associated with solar flares may be very much larger, that observed on 23 February 1956 resulting in an increase of three times for primaries in the energy range 10–100 BeV., and fifty times for primaries in the energy range 1–10 BeV. Such an effect suggests that the rapidly varying magnetic fields associated with the solar flare act as a particle accelerator. From evidence of the above type one must also conclude that under certain conditions at least a large part of the cosmic radiation which reaches the earth has its origin in the sun, and one cannot rule out the possibility that the sun normally produces the major part of the low energy radiation.

That the whole of the primary radiation cannot originate from the sun, nor be accelerated in the rapidly varying magnetic fields associated with sunspots and solar flares, is clear from energy considerations. For, even if one supposes that the whole of the low energy radiation originates from the sun, one is forced to assume some sort of suitable magnetic field around the solar system, which imprisons the radiation in such a way that it becomes more or less uniformly distributed in direction. Even assuming a rather high value for such a field, it would be difficult to hold imprisoned particles with energies much higher than about 100 BeV. It is known, however, from studies of extensive air showers, that primaries of total energy up to 10^{10} BeV. exist in the cosmic radiation. Assuming magnetic fields of the order of magnitude of those known to exist within the galaxy, such particles would have a radius of curvature of the same order of magnitude as that of the galaxy itself. In addition, it may be remarked that there is no evidence from intensity fluctuations of solar origin of the particles responsible for the extensive air showers. On the contrary, the evidence suggests that there is a very small sidereal effect, though the statistics are such that little confidence can as yet be placed in the results. Should the effect be proved by further measurements, it would be definite evidence that at least the high energy part of the radiation has its origin outside the solar system.

If one is going to give some account of the acceleration of the particles comprising the whole of the energy spectrum of the cosmic radiation, one must find some mechanism which can fill the gap between 10^2 BeV., up to which particles can be accelerated in stellar fields associated with magnetic disturbances, and the highest observed energies. Such a mechanism was suggested by Fermi in 1949. He showed that particles emitted from stars with initial energies of a few BeV. could be accelerated in the interstellar magnetic fields to very much higher energies.

The Fermi process may be described shortly as follows. The particles of the cosmic radiation which have escaped from the immediate neighbourhood of the stars in which they are produced move in spiral paths about the lines of force of the interstellar magnetic fields. These magnetic fields originate from, and are coupled to, turbulent motions of the interstellar clouds of ionized gas. The particles are 'locked' to particular lines of force, and must follow the curvature of these in space, so that there is an interchange of energy between the cosmic ray particles and the interstellar clouds. Now, Fermi could show that, if one assumes that the motion of the clouds is quite random in all directions, the net result of the transfer of energy is that the cosmic ray particles gain energy exponentially. On the other hand, a particle can lose its energy again if it is involved in a nuclear collision in interstellar space, which will, on the average, happen about once in 6×10^7 years. The equilibrium between these two effects results in an energy spectrum which falls off according to a power law with increasing energy, and by using reasonable quantities for the various parameters which enter into the theory one may obtain good agreement with the experimental energy spectrum of the primary radiation.

A question of considerable interest is the extent to which the intensity of the cosmic radiation is constant outside the immediate solar system. On the hypothesis that the radiation arises from the stellar magnetic disturbances, and is further accelerated by the interstellar magnetic fields, so that the whole of it is trapped within the galaxy, one finds that the total energy in the galaxy going into the cosmic radiation is about 10^{-4} of that emitted in the form of starlight. For, although the observed energy fluxes of the cosmic radiation and the starlight are about the same, photons cannot be trapped within the galaxy by magnetic fields and will escape after about 10^3 years. On the other hand, if one assumes that the low energy radiation is locally produced in the sun and trapped within the solar system, then one may assume that a very much smaller proportion of the total energy in the galaxy exists in the form of cosmic radiation.

The above discussion gives a very brief account of some of the ideas about the origin of the cosmic radiation which are much discussed at the time of writing. However, it should be pointed out that there are few fields in physics or astrophysics within which the accepted ideas change so quickly or so radically as that under discussion. It is therefore necessary to treat any ideas on this subject with very considerable reserve.

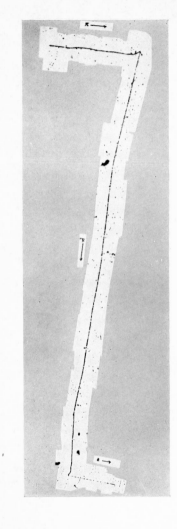

PLATE I. A π^+-meson is brought to rest in the emulsion, and decays with the emission of a μ^+-meson. This is, in turn, arrested, and decays with the emission of an electron (From Powell, *Reports on Progress in Physics*, Vol. XIII, 350 (1950))

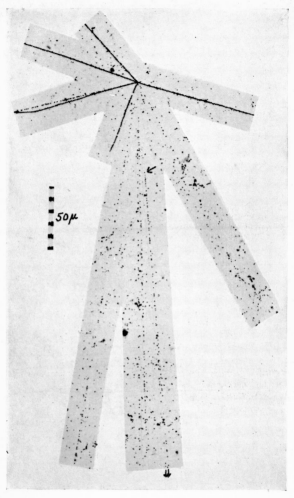

PLATE II. A 6 + 4n star observed in a nuclear emulsion exposed to the cosmic radiation. Of particular interest is the electron pair associated with the event. This is marked by small arrows. It is probably due to the conversion of a photon from the decay of a π^0-meson produced in the interaction

(From Carlson *et al.*, *Phil. Mag.*, **41**, 701 (1950))

meson penetrates a lead plate placed across the cloud chamber, discharging the counter at the centre, which controls the expansion. After emerging from the lead, it is stopped in gas of the chamber, no secondary particle being visible. Measurement of the curvature of the track in the magnetic field before and after the penetration of the lead allows one to estimate the energy loss in the plate, and this, in conjunction with the range, allows its mass to be determined

(From Neddermeyer and Anderson, *Phys. Rev.*, **54**, 88 (1938))

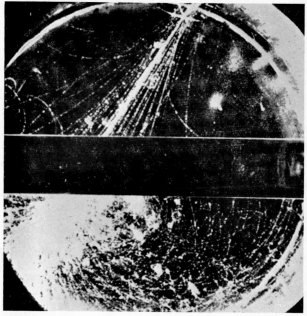

PLATE IV. A shower of mesons, electrons and photons from a very high energy interaction outside the chamber penetrates the lead plate. The cascade shower from the electron photon component obscures most of the details in the lower half of the chamber. One of the shower particles causes a secondary interaction shortly after entering the chamber (From Butler *et al.*, *Proc. Phys. Soc.*, **63A**, 145 (1950))

CHAPTER 4

High Energy Nuclear Interactions

One of the most important aspects of the cosmic radiation is the role which it plays as a source of high energy particles. Discoveries in the field of cosmic ray physics have frequently pioneered the work of the big accelerators, and have supplied valuable information on the energies required for particular studies and so played a very important part in stimulating the design of machines suitable, first for producing π-mesons, and today for producing the heavy mesons. At the same time, a detailed knowledge of the interactions which take place in the atmosphere is essential to an understanding of the effects associated with the dissipation of the energy of the primary radiation.

Nucleon-nucleon collisions

Most of the interactions initiated by high energy nucleons in the atmosphere or in nuclear emulsions flown at high altitudes take place between an incoming proton and an air or emulsion nucleus which is commonly much heavier than hydrogen. The analysis of such events is complicated by the fact that it is difficult to separate the individual processes within the nucleus; it will therefore be simplest to begin the discussion of nuclear interactions by considering simple nucleon-nucleon collisions.

Consider, then, a collision between a proton at rest in the laboratory system and a proton which approaches with a total energy $E_p = M_p c^2 \gamma_p$, where $\gamma_p = 1/\sqrt{1 - \beta^2}$. In the system of coordinates in which the centre of mass is at rest, the C-system, the total energy of each of the protons

65

is $M_p c^2 \gamma_p'$, or γ_p', if we take as the unit of energy the proton's rest-energy, where $\gamma_p' = \sqrt{(\gamma_p + 1)/2}$. The total available energy in the C-system (i.e. the sum of the *kinetic energies* of the two protons) is $2(\gamma_p' - 1)$. If this energy is insufficient to supply the rest mass of a meson, no meson creation can take place, and the total kinetic energy of the colliding particles will be the same after the collision as before it. Such collisions will be termed elastic. Collisions in which mesons are created are termed inelastic, and the degree of inelasticity is K, where $\varepsilon = 2K(\gamma_p' - 1)$ is the energy which is actually used in the creation of mesons, of whatever sort.

When $2(M_p/M_\pi).(\gamma_p' - 1) < 1$, no mesons can be created. Above this threshold mesons will be created in a few of the interactions, but the majority of interactions will become inelastic only at rather high energies, when $\gamma_p \geqslant 6$. Below $\gamma_p \sim 2$ has for some years been the domain of machine physics, and the region has been intensively studied. A great deal of detailed information is thus available on the cross-sections and types of interactions in this region. The cross-section for meson production rises very slowly with increasing primary energy above the threshold, so that even when γ_p is 20 per cent. larger than at the threshold, the cross-section for inelastic scattering is only 10^{-2} that for elastic scattering. The two cross-sections become comparable when

$$\gamma_p = 1.8 \ (E_p = 1.7 \ \text{BeV.}: \gamma_p' = 1.18).$$

Since the completion of the 'Cosmotron' in Brookhaven in 1953–4 it has been possible to study experimentally the production of mesons by simple nucleon-nucleon inter-actions at energies which correspond to the lower energy end of the spectrum of cosmic radiation. In particular, a detailed study has been made of the interactions produced in a hydrogen-filled diffusion chamber by neutrons in the energy range from 1 to 2 BeV. At these energies a large number of three-pronged events were found which could be analysed by measurements of the relative angles and momenta and which were shown to include events of the three types:

(1) $n + p \longrightarrow p + p + \pi^-$
(2) $n + p \longrightarrow p + p + \pi^- + \pi^0$
(3) $n + p \longrightarrow p + n + \pi^- + \pi^+$.

No events with five outgoing particles were found in this experiment, so that it was necessary to conclude that only single and double meson production were of importance at these energies. As many as five charged mesons have since been observed to be produced at one time in more energetic collisions. Such multiple events are responsible for the so-called 'penetrating showers' which are observed in the cosmic radiation.

In addition to the actual numbers of particles produced, the Brookhaven team investigated the momentum and angular distributions of the emerging particles in the C-system, and compared these with those predicted by Fermi's statistical theory of meson production. The momentum distribution was found to agree well with the theory, but the angular distributions showed detailed features which were not in agreement, such as a marked tendency, in reactions of the third type, for the π^--meson to be emitted in a forward direction, while the π^+-meson was emitted backwards. The total distributions, however, showed a peaking backwards and forwards which was in qualitative agreement with the theory. It was also found that the ratio of double production events to single production events in the energy region studied was about twenty times higher than that predicted by Fermi's theory. However, that the Fermi theory does not hold very exactly at energies of a few BeV. is not very surprising, for it is a statistical theory of very high energy interactions, and does not take into account the detailed mechanism of the interaction.

The two very important results of the Brookhaven experiment are first that multiple production of mesons can and does take place in comparatively low energy nucleon-nucleon collisions, and secondly, that one cannot necessarily expect that the angular distribution of the emitted mesons will even be approximately isotropic in the C-system. The first point clears up an argument that has raged for many years as to whether in nucleon-nucleus collisions the mesons were produced one at a time in a series of individual nucleon-nucleon encounters within the target nucleus, or whether they were mostly produced in the first collision.

The distributions in momentum and angle in the C-system are of great interest in the comparison of the experimental results with those of theory. In principle, if the primary energy is known, it is only necessary to measure the momenta and angles of emission of the emitted mesons with respect to the primary direction, to be able to calculate the distributions in the C-system. While this can be done in the machine experiments, where the primary energies are exactly known, in most of the examples found in emulsions or cloud chambers exposed to the cosmic radiation, the primary energies involved are well above the limits of measurement imposed by the experimental techniques at present available. On the other hand, if the angular and energy distributions in C-system are known, then it is possible to use the same measurements to determine the energy of the primary, and some rather general results can be shown to follow from this. For example, it can be shown that if the distributions in the C-system are symmetrical about the plane perpendicular to the line of flight of the incoming particle, and if the velocities of the emitted particles in the C-system are close to that of light, then the angles η_f and η_{1-f} in the laboratory system, where η_f is the half-angle of the cone within which a fraction f of the shower particles is emitted, are related to the primary energy by the equation:

$$\gamma_p = 2/\eta_f . \eta_{1-f}, \qquad (4.1)$$

and in particular, if the median angle, $\eta_{1/2}$, is measured $(f = 1 - f = \frac{1}{2})$ then we can write:

$$\gamma_p = 2/\eta_{1/2}^2. \qquad (4.2)$$

Relation (4.2) is particularly important, for it has, up to the time of writing, provided the most important means of estimating the energies involved in the very high energy events caused by the cosmic radiation. We shall later discuss some of the limits on its use, but it should here be remarked that it is only strictly valid for pure nucleon-nucleon collisions.

Nucleon-nucleus interactions

As mentioned above, the vast majority of the events which can be studied in the emulsion are of the nucleon-nucleus, rather than the nucleon-nucleon type. The same is also true of cloud-chamber studies, for here most of the events take place in absorbers placed either in or above the chamber. When considering such events two possibilities arise; either the incoming nucleon interacts with the nucleus as a whole or a group of nucleons within the nucleus, or else it interacts with a single nucleon. If the first suggestion were correct, then one would expect very large differences between the nucleon-nucleon and nucleon-nucleus types of interaction. The experimental evidence, on the other hand, suggests no such differences, and, in fact, interactions taking place in the CNO group of nuclei often possess characteristics, as far as the shower particles are concerned, which are very similar to those which were concluded to be characteristic of nucleon-nucleon collisions. Hence the assumption is made that the incoming nucleon interacts first with a single nucleon of the target nucleus. We do not, however, exclude the possibility that some of the particles leaving the first interaction may interact with other nucleons of the target nucleus before they escape from the nucleus.

When the primary energy is too low for any meson

creation, the incoming nucleus will be scattered elastically one or more times in its passage through the nucleus, knocking on one or two nucleons and giving smaller quantities of energy to others, which will not escape from the nucleus immediately, but will share their energy among the remaining nucleons of the nucleus. This surplus energy is eventually dissipated by the nucleus 'evaporating' a number of low energy nucleons or nuclear fragments, leading, in the emulsion, to a number of black tracks emerging from the disintegration. The angular distribution of the evaporation particles in the laboratory system is isotropic, for they are emitted from a system which is at rest in the laboratory. It is important to realize that the time between the collision and the emission of the evaporation fragments is essentially long compared with the time of passage of the incoming nucleon across the nucleus.

If the energy of the primary nucleon is above the threshold for meson production, mesons may be produced in some of the individual nucleon-nucleon encounters. If the struck nucleus is small, or if the nucleon which is struck lies close to the edge of the nucleus, then the mesons and knock-on nucleons will escape from the nucleus with very little further interaction, so that the shower produced will look very similar to that produced by an elementary nucleon-nucleon collision with the addition of a small number of black evaporation tracks emerging from the point of distintegration. On the other hand, if the struck nucleus is large, a cascade process may be set up, so that further mesons are also produced in secondary nucleon-nucleon collisions. In addition, the mesons themselves might be either scattered, elastically, or inelastically, during their passage through the nucleus, or they might be reabsorbed before they escape from the nucleus if the nucleus were much less transparent to high energy mesons than it is to nucleons. The various possibilities can only be sorted out experimentally.

Experimental evidence

(1) *Intermediate energies*†

The experimental evidence on nuclear interactions at intermediate energies still rests mainly on the results obtained from the Cosmic Radiation, but during the past two years considerable contributions have also been made by the machine groups at Berkeley and Brookhaven, who have had at their disposal beams of protons, neutrons and π-mesons of known energies in the region between 1 and 6 BeV. Their experiments have confirmed definitely many results previously suspected, and at the same time they have enabled more detailed accounts to be given of some of the elementary processes involved. Some of the most important results from Brookhaven have already been discussed above.

While the Brookhaven results are of great interest in that they demonstrate very clearly the elementary processes involved in more complex nuclear interactions, the information obtained from studies of nucleon-nucleus collisions is of more direct interest for an understanding of the phenomena associated with the development and degeneration of the cosmic radiation in the atmosphere. Here most of the detailed work has been done using nuclear emulsions flown to great altitudes, and studying the disintegrations caused in them by incoming protons and by π-mesons created in, or in the immediate neighbourhood of, the stack. Few π-mesons will enter from the atmosphere, for, as a consequence of their short lifetime, they decay close to the place where they are created.

† Considerable confusion exists in the use of the terms 'low energy', 'high energy', &c., and in what follows the term 'low energy' will be used for events in which the primary energy is less than 0·35 BeV.; 'intermediate energy' for those between 0·35 BeV. and 10 BeV.; 'high energy' for those between 10 BeV. and 100 BeV. and 'very high energy' for those whose primary energy is greater than 100 BeV.

It should be noted that in such studies most of the inter-actions are with the silver or bromine nuclei of the emulsion, for the geometric cross-section for collisions with these nuclei is three times larger than that for collisions with the CNO group of nuclei. As there are in the emulsion very few atoms of atomic number between 8 and 35 (see Table 2.1), it is possible to make a partial separation of the data by assigning all stars with eight or more black evaporation tracks to interactions involving (AgBr) nuclei. The remainder will also include a considerable proportion of interactions which also belong to the above group, even though it contains all those which take place in the nuclei of the light elements.

In emulsion work, the tracks emerging from nuclear dis-integrations are usually divided into three classes:

(1) 'Shower Particles', whose grain density does not ex-ceed 1·4 times the plateau value for singly charged particles, corresponding to $\beta = 0·77$ for singly charged particles and kinetic energies of 80 MeV. and 500 MeV. for π-mesons and protons respectively.

(2) 'Grey Tracks', where the grain density lies between 1·4 and 8 times the plateau value of the grain density, corresponding, for singly charged particles, to protons of energy between 25 MeV. and 500 MeV., and to π-mesons of energy less than 80 MeV.

(3) 'Black Tracks' have a grain density higher than 8 times the plateau value. They can be produced by protons of energy less than 25 MeV., by deuterons and tritons of energy less than 50 MeV. and 75 MeV. respectively, by α-particles of energy less than 800 MeV., and by any frag-ments of charge higher than 2, which may occasionally be emitted during the evaporation of the struck nucleus.

Each star is characterized by two figures, N_h and n_s, corresponding respectively to the number of black + the number of grey tracks emitted from the disintegration, and to the number of shower particle tracks, together with a symbol denoting the nature of the particle primary to the interaction. Thus the star shown in Plate II would be classified as $6 + 4n$: 6 black or grey tracks, 4 shower particle tracks, and no visible primary particle track, indicating that the event was probably due to a fast neutron.

The value of N_h depends not only on the energy which is dissipated in the struck nucleus by evaporation but will also be a function of the primary energy and the size of the nucleus. In the emulsion there is a very large gap between the atomic weights of the light elements (C, N, O) and the heavy elements (Ag, Br) in which, as we have seen, the majority of the interactions take place. Thus, if $N_h \geqslant 8$ it is almost certain that the interaction took place in a silver or bromine nucleus.

In cosmic ray exposures the nature of the primary particle is not known, and it can be determined by scattering-grain-density measurements only if its energy is less than about 1 BeV. Both protons and π-mesons in the energy range 0·35–1 BeV. have been observed to create stars, and both types of particles are known to be present at higher energies in the cosmic radiation. Thus particles of energy higher than 1 BeV. can be either protons or π-mesons, but the majority will in fact be protons, for very few π-mesons can enter the plates from the outside atmosphere at high altitudes, as they decay in flight close to that place in the atmosphere where they were created. Most of the π-meson primaries can therefore be assumed to have been created in the plates themselves, or in the immediate surrounding material. Direct measurements in the energy range 0·35–1 BeV., supplemented by extrapolation to higher energies, suggest that about 15 per cent. of the high energy primaries are π-mesons.

Investigations of the charged shower particles in cosmic ray meson showers show that about 80 per cent. of the observed shower particles are π-mesons, the other 20 per cent. being fast recoil protons from the individual meson-producing reactions. In addition, one must remember that the number of neutrons produced, both at low and high

F

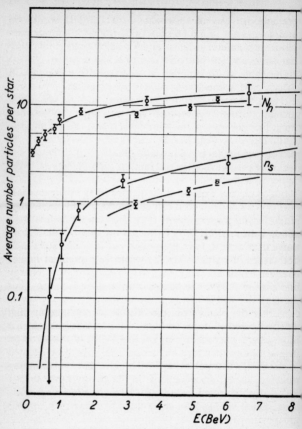

FIG. 15. N_h and n_s as a function of the energy of the primary particle for stars caused by cosmic ray and machine primaries. (Based on data from Camerini *et al.*, *Phil. Mag.*, **42**, 1241 (1951), and Johnson, *Phys. Rev.*, **99**, 1049 (1955))

energies, is expected to be comparable to that of protons, and, as mentioned below, neutral mesons are also created. None of these neutral particles are directly observed in the emulsion, so that their presence must be indirectly inferred, either from considerations of missing energy or from indirect experiments.

The observed variations of N_h and n_s as a function of primary energy, for cosmic ray stars, are illustrated in Fig. 15. For comparison, the results obtained from a similar machine experiment, in which the energy of the primary particles was accurately known, are shown. The fact that the points from the machine experiment lie a little lower is probably due to two main causes. Firstly, there is some evidence that at high energies scattering measurements tend to lead to too low an estimate of the energy, due to random, very small dislocations in the emulsion. A second effect, which may cause a small contribution in the same direction, is that there is a proportion of events among the cosmic ray stars with π-meson primaries which have a greater centre of mass energy in a collision with a nucleon for a given kinetic energy in the laboratory system than have protons of the same kinetic energy.

As would be expected, both N_h and n_s rise as a function of the primary energy over the whole energy range considered. At very high energies, of course, the value of N_h must become constant, for it cannot exceed the atomic number of the target nuclei. A second point to notice is that over a very large part of the energy range the number of charged π-mesons produced is considerably less than one, due to the fact that mesons are created in only a small proportion of the total number of nucleon-nucleon encounters, the remainder being elastic. As the proportion of elastic encounters decreases with increasing primary energy, so the average number of charged mesons created increases. This effect is illustrated in Fig. 16, in which the proportion of the total number of stars observed which have no associated shower particles is plotted as a function of the primary energy. It can be seen that for primary energies less than 1·6 BeV. (total energy $\gamma_p = 2·7$) more than half the primaries do not produce secondary shower particles.

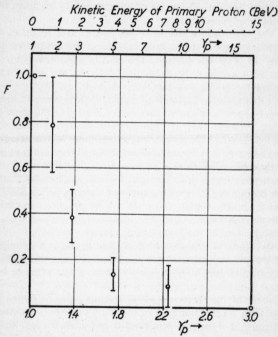

FIG. 16. The proportion of O_p stars as a function of the primary energy. (From Camerini *et al.*, *Phil. Mag.*, **42**, 1241 (1951))

In addition to the charged π-mesons which are created in nuclear disintegrations, neutral π-mesons are also produced. Their presence has now been demonstrated by many different experiments, both in the field of machine work and in that of the cosmic radiation. If the energy spectrum of the cosmic ray photons observed at high altitudes, where any effects due to cascade formation could reasonably be expected to be small, is measured, it is found that it has a sharp peak in the region of about 70 MeV., and, in addition, the property that the square root of the product of the two energies corresponding to any given intensity is a constant, whose value is equal to the energy of the maximum of intensity. This property is a characteristic of the spectrum produced by the Doppler effect from the monochromatic radiation emitted by sources moving with some arbitrary energy spectrum in the laboratory system. It is easy to show that the unique energy of the photons in the centre of mass of the emitting system is equal to that of the maximum of the observed spectrum. On the assumption that the moving sources which emit the radiation are π^0-mesons of rest energy $2 \cdot E_{max}. \approx 140$ MeV. $\approx 270 m_e$ it is possible to deduce their spectrum at production from the photon spectrum and compare this with that found under similar experimental conditions for the charged mesons. The results of such a comparison, from an emulsion experiment, are shown in Fig. 17. The observed close similarity of the spectra is considered to provide very strong evidence in favour of the production of the neutral mesons in the same interactions, and by the same processes, as those in which the charged mesons are created.

The ratio, $\phi = N_{\pi^0}/N_{\pi^\mp}$ has been studied directly, by searching the volume of emulsion in the vicinity of stars with $n_s \geqslant 3$ for electron pairs which could have been produced by photons which were secondary to π^0-mesons produced in the original disintegration. As a result of the very short lifetime of the π^0-meson ($\approx 5 \cdot 10^{-15}$ sec.) the axis of such 'related' pairs is expected to point in a direction passing very close to the centre of the distintegration, for the neutral meson can only travel a very short distance ($\sim 5 \mu$) before decay. In this way a value of $\phi = 0.45 \pm 0.10$ was obtained. That is to say, π^-, π^+ and π^0-mesons are all

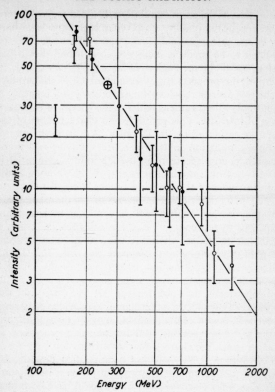

FIG. 17. Comparison of the spectra of charged and neutral mesons produced by cosmic-ray induced inter-actions. Charged mesons: O. Neutral mesons:

created in about equal numbers. This is the type of result which one would expect from charge independence of nuclear forces.

The effects of secondary interactions produced within

the target nucleus may be studied by separating the data according to the number of heavy prongs associated with the stars. At a given primary energy stars with a small number of evaporation prongs may be assumed to have been created either in light nuclei or in such a way in the heavy nuclei that the energy transferred to the nucleus was

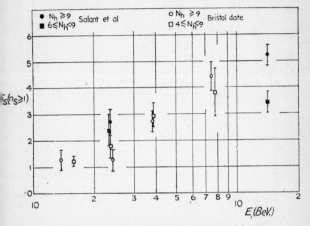

FIG. 18. The average number of shower particles as a function of the primary energy. (From Camerini *et al.*, *Phil. Mag.*, **42**, 1261 (1951))

small, which ensures that the number of secondary interactions must have been small. Similarly, one may assume that if the number of evaporation particles produced is large, then the number of secondary processes in the nucleus must also have been of some importance, for a much larger energy has been transferred to the nucleons which were not directly struck by the primary. The average number of shower particles is plotted as a function of energy in Fig. 18, for large and small values of N_h. The effect of the second generation may be clearly seen at high energies.

The variation of the median angle of showers as a function of their multiplicity is shown in Fig. 19. The data have been divided into two groups corresponding to $N_h < 7$ and

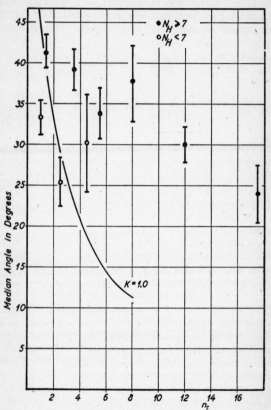

FIG. 19. The median angle of meson showers as a function of the multiplicity, n_s. (From Camerini *et al.*, *Phil. Mag.*, **42**, 1241 (1951))

$N_h \geqslant 7$, and a curve corresponding to the equation $\gamma_p = 2/\eta_{1/2}{}^2$, obtained above for single nucleon-nucleon collisions, and assuming an inelasticity $K = 1$, is drawn in for comparison. There is good agreement between the curve and the angular distribution from the stars with few evaporation tracks, showing that secondary scattering, or production, of mesons is not an important effect in collisions involving light nuclei. The much broader angular distribution of the shower particles from those stars with large values of N_h must be interpreted as being a consequence of the scattering of the created mesons within the nucleus, before they escape, and possibly also, in part, of the production of secondary showers within the nucleus by particles emerging from the first nucleon-nucleon collision. That secondary production takes place in the heavy nuclei of the emulsion may be deduced from the fact that at a given primary energy there is a positive correlation between the number of shower particles observed and the number of evaporation particles from the target nucleus.

A second question of importance is whether any considerable proportion of the newly created mesons are re-absorbed in their passage out of a large nucleus. That the effect is not very large may be seen from the above mentioned fact that the effect of the production of a second generation of shower particles is clearly seen at higher energies (Fig. 18). A good deal of further evidence is available from experiments in which π-mesons are the primary particles creating the showers. These experiments show that at energies up to about 160 MeV. about half the mesons are absorbed in their collisions with nuclei, but that the effects resulting from absorption are very much smaller at higher energies. At the same time it has been demonstrated that further π-mesons can be created in high energy π-meson-nucleon interactions, so that not only the scattered primary nucleon (in a nucleon-induced interaction) and the recoil nucleon can create a second generation of nucleons in a large nucleus, but also the more energetic of the π-mesons emerging from the first nucleon-nucleon interaction.

Several attempts have been made to measure the angular distribution of the shower particles in the centre of mass system, but no detailed information, apart from that obtained at Brookhaven, has so far been obtained. At the time of writing, the evidence is such that it is consistent with an isotropic distribution, but it applies, essentially, to nucleon-nucleus collisions in which the original distribution may be smeared out by the secondary scattering which takes place before the created mesons escape from the nucleus.

Information on the cross-sections for nucleon-produced interactions has come mainly from counter studies, a number of which have been made. Apart from confirming that the cross-sections of neutrons and protons are very little different, these experiments have shown that the cross-sections tend to a geometrical value $(\hbar/M_\pi c).A^{2/3}$ (where M_π is the mass of the π-meson and A the number of nucleons in the struck nucleus) as the energy of the incident particles increases. At lower energies the cross-section is more closely geometrical for heavy target nuclei than for light ones, but even in the region of 1 BeV. incident energy it is already rather close to the geometrical value, provided, of course, one takes both elastic and inelastic processes into account.

(2) *High and very high energy regions*

The region of energy above 10 BeV. is perhaps the most interesting of the various energy regions so far studied in nuclear physics, partly because one is here sufficiently above the threshold energies of all the known processes for them to be able to occur rather frequently, and partly because it is, as yet, only very superficially examined. At these high energies most of the methods of measurement of velocity and energy which can be used at lower energies, based essentially on the electromagnetic interactions of charged particles in their passage through matter, become rather ineffective. Insufficient is as yet known about nuclear interactions to allow their effects to be used as a basis for accurate methods of measurement. At the same time, the rapid decrease of the intensity of the primary cosmic radiation as a function of increasing energy means that events in the high and very high energy regions are rare, so that the labour involved in collecting sufficient data is particularly onerous. There have been published, however, a certain amount of data, and a few events in the 1,000 BeV. range have been analysed in detail.

That secondary processes are important in the high energy range in interactions involving heavy nuclei has been shown by the Bristol group who plotted the average energy per shower particle as a function of the number of shower particles for different values of N_h (Fig. 20). It is seen that for high values of N_h the average energy of the shower particles is much lower than for low values of N_h, indicating that the particles lose a considerable proportion of their energy in secondary interactions before they finally escape from the nucleus. Also, for a given primary energy the number of secondary particles produced is probably larger for events taking place in heavy nuclei, so that, at high energies, the multiplicity, n_s, is a very much less definite indication of the primary energy than for similar events in the intermediate energy region, where the energies of the particles emerging from the first collision will very often not be sufficient to produce further mesons.

The fact that a rather large proportion of the very high energy showers which have been observed in emulsions are associated with very few evaporation fragments has been explained in two ways. Firstly, many of the interactions have been attributed to collisions taking place at the edge of the nucleus, which leave the rest of the nucleus comparatively undisturbed. Alternatively, Roesler and McCusker have suggested that at the very high energies involved the angular distribution of the particles emerging from the first interaction is so highly collimated in the laboratory system,

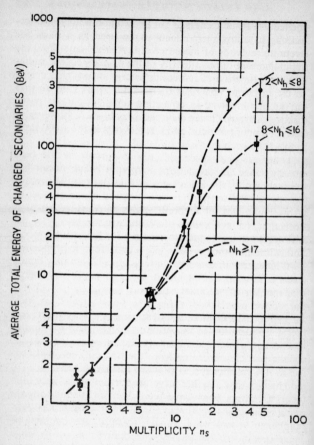

FIG. 20. The average energy of meson shower particles as a function of the multiplicity n_s. (From Daniel et al., Phil. Mag., 43, 753 (1952))

and the effects of scattering are so small, that, in effect, the incoming nucleus is able to punch a clean hole through the target nucleus, so that only those nucleons which lie within the cylindrical tunnel defined by the angular width of the initial shower will be involved in the meson-producing processes. In both of the explanations given above the reason for the small excitation of the target nucleus is the same; the very high collimation of the secondary particles produced in the first collision is such that only a very small proportion of the nucleons in the nucleus receive any energy at all, and these tend to receive so much that they are all removed cleanly from the nucleus. It can, of course, happen, that a high energy particle, emitted backwards in the centre of mass system of the primary collision, can have a sufficiently high energy and a direction in the laboratory system such that a very large amount of energy is transferred to the target nucleus, so that the number of evaporation particles comes close to the maximum possible.

At present the evidence on the nature of the shower particles produced in high and very high energy collisions is somewhat contradictory. What is certain is that by far the largest number of them are, as at lower energies, π-mesons. Several attempts have been made to study the proportion of heavier mesons among the shower particles by measuring the ratio of the total number of charged shower particles to the number of π^0-mesons produced in individual interactions. On the assumption that charge independence of nuclear forces holds rigidly, so that the ratio of charged π-mesons to neutral mesons in showers of high multiplicity will be 2, one may deduce from the number of π^0-mesons, obtained from the observed related electron pairs and cascade showers directly associated with the disintegration, the proportion of shower particles which are not charged π-mesons. The results obtained by this method have been rather contradictory, some workers finding that the proportion of π-mesons was very much higher than that of all other types of particles, while others have found that the number of heavy mesons, &c., produced in such interactions is not very much smaller than that of charged π-mesons. The method rests on the assumption that the only important source of high energy photons from the interactions is the decay of the directly produced neutral mesons.

That heavy mesons and hyperons do exist among the shower particles is known from direct measurements on tracks lying on the outer edge of the shower cone. These are those tracks which have been emitted backwards in the centre of mass system of the disintegration, and which are thus much slower in the laboratory system, so that it is frequently possible to make an approximate determination of their mass by multiple scattering and grain-count measurements. Such determinations have provided some information on the question of the rate of production of particles other than π-mesons in high energy events, but the statistics up to the time of writing are not sufficient to allow any particularly detailed conclusions to be drawn. If one takes into account all the interactions produced by the primary radiation, it is possible to state that the total production of heavy unstable particles is only about 1 per cent. of that of π-mesons. Apart from the heavy mesons and hyperons, two examples of antiprotons have been found to emerge, both with very low kinetic energies, from interactions caused by high energy protons of the cosmic radiation.

We have seen that if the event can be regarded as a single nucleon-nucleon interaction, with no or very few associated evaporation particles, the energy of the primary particle may be estimated from the relation:

$$\gamma_p = 2/\eta_{1/2}^2 \,.$$

However, in many of the events which have been analysed in detail, the value of N_h has been large and there is clear evidence for secondary interactions within the target nucleus, so that the median angle of the shower will lead to an estimate of the energy which is much too low, and other methods must be used to obtain a more accurate estimate of the energy. The same is also true of events in which the multiplicity of the shower particles is small, so that the measurement of the median angle itself is subject to very considerable uncertainty. Several methods have been tried, but perhaps those that have produced the most reliable results are the study of the interactions caused by the shower particles themselves, which, being of lower energy than the primary, are more amenable to the usual methods of analysis which are known from the intermediate energy region, and the study of the electron cascades produced by the photons resulting from the decay of the π^0-mesons from the original interaction. From these it is possible to estimate, on the basis of cascade theory, both the energies and the number of π^0-mesons produced. It is then reasonable to assume, at least for events of high multiplicity, that the average energy of the charged π-mesons is the same as that of the neutral π-mesons. In this way a direct estimate of the energy of the shower primary may be obtained.

Very little is known about the angular and momentum distributions of the shower particles in the centre of mass system of the colliding nucleons. In the very high energy region the existing evidence suggests that there is a strong forward-backward concentration about the line of flight of the incoming particle. There is also some evidence to the effect that about one in ten of the mesons is emitted with an energy which is about half of the total available. At lower energies there exists evidence from cloud-chamber experiments that when the primary energy is $\approx$ 30 BeV. the distribution in the centre of mass system is approximately isotropic.

In the high and very high energy regions the connection between the multiplicity of the shower and the primary energy does not seem to be so marked as in the intermediate energy region. Very large fluctuations for a given range of primary energies have been observed, and it is possible that these correspond in some way to variations of the impact parameter of the collision. For events with primary energies in the region of 2,000–3,000 BeV. which have no evaporation fragments associated with them, a singly charged primary, and an even number of shower particles, so that they could have been due to pure proton-proton collisions, charged particle multiplicities as low as four and as high as 30 have been observed by the Bristol group. The experience of other groups has been rather similar. In events associated with a large number of evaporation fragments, on the other hand, the number of shower particles produced tends to be very high, and examples in which over 100 shower particles are emitted have been observed. Here, however, there is no doubt that a considerable proportion of the shower particles are produced by the secondary interactions within the nucleus.

Nucleus-nucleus interactions

Interactions between the energetic incoming primary nuclei of the cosmic radiation and the nuclei of the atoms of the atmosphere or the detecting apparatus are much more complicated than the nucleon-nucleus interactions discussed above, and are thus not of great use in obtaining a fundamental understanding of the nuclear processes taking place at very high energies. On the other hand, some knowledge of the type of effects which are produced in such interactions is essential to an understanding of the development of the cosmic radiation in the atmosphere, and, at the very highest energies, to an understanding of some of the extensive air showers observed in the lower half of the atmosphere.

The cross-section for the interaction of heavy nuclei at high energies has been measured in glass by Bradt and Peters, and in brass by Kaplon and his co-workers. It is found to be well represented by the empirical formula:

$$\sigma = \pi(r_1 + r_2 - 2\Delta r)^2,$$

where the subscripts refer to the two colliding nuclei and where

$$r = 1\cdot45 \times 10^{-13}A^{1/3} \text{ cm.} \quad \text{and} \quad \Delta r = 0\cdot85 \times 10^{-13} \text{ cm.}$$

As glass consists mainly of silicon and oxygen the formula should be directly applicable to air.

We have seen that in ordinary nucleon-nucleus collisions it is possible to divide the various particles produced into various classes: shower particles, recoil protons or grey tracks, evaporation fragments, which consist about equally of protons and α-particles of a few MeV. kinetic energy, and finally a recoil fragment, whose kinetic energy in the laboratory system is often so low that it is not easy to distinguish it in an emulsion, which has a high stopping power. Now consider what happens when a heavy nucleus strikes a proton in the atmosphere or emulsion. In the centre of mass system of the heavy nucleus, it is the proton which strikes it, so that in order to predict the appearance of the event in the emulsion it is only necessary to transform the ordinary nucleon-nucleus collision from the rest system of the heavy nucleus to that of the laboratory. The appearance of the shower particles will not be markedly changed. Evaporation fragments of the incoming nucleus will continue with a very small scattering and with velocity little changed, while the recoil nucleus will appear as the original nucleus, which has been partially stripped of some of its nucleons, but unchanged in velocity and direction. The tracks which were called grey tracks in the treatment of nucleon-nucleus collisions will now tend to have their velocity increased so that they may often appear as additional shower particles.

The collision between two nuclei is more complicated for now all the types of track observed in a nucleus-nucleon collision, as well as the grey tracks and evaporation fragments of the target nucleus, will appear. In such collisions it very often happens that there are many individual nucleon-nucleon encounters, which results in the greater

G

destruction of both nuclei, so that recoil fragments, both of the incoming and of the target nuclei, are absent, and the very large number of high energy recoil nucleons produced means that fewer evaporation fragments are produced from the part of the target nucleus which remains. Thus, it can happen that the colliding nuclei are completely destroyed. In only about 50 per cent. of the observed examples is there enough left of the incoming nucleus to evaporate.

The evaporation fragments of the incoming nucleus may, if they can be recognized, and if their angular distribution can be measured, be used to measure its energy, in rather the same way as the angular distribution of shower particles may be used to measure the energy of singly charged primaries. However, because of the difficulty of distinguishing meson and proton tracks at high energies, only those fragments of charge greater than $Z = 1$ may be used. Most of these will be α-particles. Direct studies of α-particle evaporation fragments from nuclei at rest have shown that they are emitted isotropically with a mean kinetic energy between 10 and 15 MeV., and that particles with an energy greater than 30 MeV. are very rare.

Thus the root mean square angle of the evaporation fragments of the incoming nucleus in the laboratory system is given by:

$$\sqrt{\langle \theta^2 \rangle} = (TM/3p_0{}^2)^{1/2},$$

where T is the average kinetic energy of the α-particles in the rest system, M is the mass of the proton and p_0 the momentum per nucleon of the incoming nucleus. Putting $T = 12$ MeV., we have, in the relativistic region:

$$\sqrt{\langle \theta^2 \rangle} = 0.06/\varepsilon,$$

where ε is the energy per nucleon of the incoming nucleus.

If there are only two or three evaporation α-particles they may well all be emitted forwards or backwards in the rest system of the incoming nucleus, or they may all have

energies less or greater than the assumed average energy.
These effects will lead to misestimates of the energy of the
incoming nucleus, but when the number of α-particles is
greater there is little danger of serious errors. At the same
time the assumption that an α-particle is never emitted with
an energy in the centre of mass system of the nucleus greater
than 30 MeV. allows an upper limit to the energy of the
incoming particle to be obtained, for the largest possible
angle in the laboratory system is:

$$\theta_{\text{max.}} = 0\cdot 12/\varepsilon.$$

Thus, even if all the α-particles are emitted in such a way
that they emerge from the interaction with the largest
possible angles in the laboratory system, it is not possible
to underestimate the energy by more than a factor of two.

CHAPTER 5

High Energy Electromagnetic Processes

The most important of the 'low energy' electromagnetic interactions such as ionization, multiple scattering, &c., have already been discussed in Chapter 2. In these processes the transfer of energy and momentum involved in any single interaction is usually very small compared with the energy of the incoming particle. When the energy of the incoming particle is high, a number of new types of interaction are predicted by the quantum theory of electrodynamics, in which large energies are frequently transferred in single interactions. The theory has long been well established and several excellent books on the subject have been published, to which reference is made in the list of 'Further Reading' at the end of the book. Here, it will be sufficient to give a brief phenomenological account of the processes which are of the greatest importance in the study of the cosmic radiation, and some account of the type of evidence upon which the theory is based.

Pair production

The prediction by Dirac, on the basis of the so-called 'hole' theory, that there should exist particles of single electronic positive charge and electronic mass, was followed by the discovery of such particles in the cosmic radiation. It was discovered, in agreement with the predictions, that they were created by the materialization of the energy of high energy photons, simultaneously with the creation of an ordinary negative electron. In the language of the hole theory, the process corresponds to an ordinary electron jumping from a state of negative kinetic energy to one of positive kinetic energy, leaving an unfilled place in the continuum of negative energy states, which are normally completely filled. It may be shown that such a hole would be expected to behave as a positive electron with positive kinetic energy and momentum.

Apart from pair production, photons are also known to transfer energy to matter by the photoelectric effect and the Compton effect, but at the energies of the cosmic radiation the cross-sections for both these processes are very small compared with that for pair production. The same is also true of the cross-section of high energy photons for nuclear interactions.

The threshold energy for pair production is $2m_ec^2 = 1.02$ MeV., for the process cannot take place unless the photon has sufficient energy to provide the combined mass of the two created particles. The process takes place within the coulomb field of some charged particle, which may be either an electron or the nucleus of an atom, which absorbs a certain amount of momentum, $\sim m_ec$, enabling momentum to be conserved.

We shall first consider pair production in the field of a nucleus of charge Z. Above the threshold the total cross-section rises rapidly as a function of increasing photon energy, the curve above 10 MeV. being given by the relation:

$$b_p = \frac{Z^2}{137} \cdot \left(\frac{e^2}{m_ec^2}\right)^2 \left\{\frac{28}{9} \ln\left(\frac{2h\nu}{m_ec^2}\right) - \frac{218}{7}\right\}, \quad (5.1)$$

which is valid provided that the energies of all the particles involved in the interaction, apart from the atomic nucleus, may be considered to be extreme relativistic. At energies lower than 10 MeV., where the extreme relativistic approximation is not valid, it is not possible to obtain an analytical expression for the total cross-section, and this has been calculated numerically by Bethe and Heitler. The above formula is further based on the assumption that the effects of screening of the nuclear coulomb field by the surrounding electron field is negligible. At very high energies this assumption is not valid, and formula (5.1) may not be used. When the screening is complete, one obtains another analytical formula for the total cross-section:

$$b_p = \frac{Z^2}{137} \cdot \left(\frac{e^2}{m_e c^2}\right)^2 \left\{\frac{28}{9} \ln (183 Z^{-1/3}) - \frac{2}{27}\right\}, \quad (5.2)$$

which is seen to be independent of the energy of the photon.

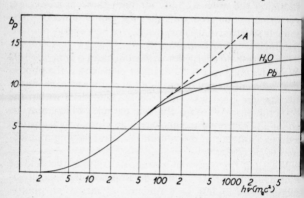

FIG. 21. The variation of the total cross-section for pair production by photons, as a function of the photon energy, in water and lead. b_p is plotted in units of $(Z^2/137)(e^2/m_e c^2)^2$. Curve A shows the effect of neglecting screening. (From Bethe and Heitler, *Proc. Roy. Soc.*, **146A**, 83 (1934))

It should be noted that, in air, complete screening is effective when the energy of the photon exceeds a few hundred MeV., so that the formula which is of most importance in cosmic ray work is (5.2), not (5.1). In the region between those in which (5.1) and (5.2) are valid, where there is incomplete screening, no analytical solution can be obtained, and resort must again be had to numerical methods. Fig. 21 illustrates the variation of the cross-section as a function of photon energy in water and lead, and illustrates the effect of screening at high energies.

Due to the large mass of any nucleus compared with that of an electron, very little energy is involved in the momentum transfer to the nucleus in the interaction, so that, apart from pairs created by photons whose energy lies only just above the threshold, one may write for the energy of the pair:

$$E' + E'' = h\nu - 2m_e c^2.$$

The electrons tend to be emitted in the forward direction, within a solid angle in the laboratory system $\delta \approx m_e c^2/h\nu$. Although there is some correlation between the energy at which an electron is emitted, and its direction of emission, the fact that the nucleus takes up a small share of the momentum involved implies that the relation between the two quantities is not rigidly determined. Thus, although one can say in general that electrons of lower energy from pairs created by photons of some fixed energy will tend to be emitted at larger angles, it is found that in fact the electrons of any chosen energy are emitted with a certain continuous angular distribution.

The division of the available energy between the newly created electrons of the pair is, as a rule, uneven. In fact, if one plots, for some given photon energy, the differential cross-section for one of the particles (say the positive electron) to obtain a given fraction of the total available energy $(h\nu - 2m_e c^2)$, one finds a broad distribution which rises very steeply at zero and one. When the photon energy is low, less than about 10 MeV., the curve has a broad maximum at 0·5, but as the total energy increases the maximum becomes flatter and flatter, finally giving place to two almost symmetrical † maxima, which, with further increase in the photon's energy, move out towards the

† In most existing calculations the Born approximation is used, so that no difference is made between the positive and negative electron's cross-sections, and the curves so obtained are symmetric.

extremities of the curve. A typical curve, showing also some experimental results from the measurement of the differential cross-section, is reproduced in Fig. 23a.

As mentioned above, pair production by photons in the field of an electron may also take place. The cross-section per atomic electron is equal to that of a proton, so that in order to take this effect into account in the total cross-section for a given material, one should write $Z(Z + 1)$ instead of Z^2 in formulae (5.1) and (5.2). It is clear that the correction is most important in the very light elements, being of the order of 10 per cent. for carbon, but only about 2 per cent. for silver.

Bremsstrahlung

Apart from energy loss by ionization, a charged particle may also lose energy while traversing matter by the process known as *Bremsstrahlung*: the emission of a photon of energy comparable to that of the incident particle itself. Classically, the effect corresponds to the emission of radiation by a charged particle when it is accelerated. The quantum mechanical treatment of the effect is found to be mathematically very closely similar to that of pair production, and, as mentioned above for pair production, exact theoretical cross-sections can only be obtained analytically in certain energy regions which correspond roughly with those which we have found for pair production.

The differential cross-section for the emission by an electron of some given energy of a photon taking a certain fraction of the total available energy is illustrated in Fig. 23b. The curve shown is for electrons of 372 MeV., but at all energies the general features are similar, the curve being a little flatter if the electron energy is higher, so that there is a larger probability for the emission of a photon taking a very large fraction of the available energy, and rather steeper at lower energies.

In the high energy region, where the nucleus may be considered to be completely screened, the rate of energy loss to *Bremsstrahlung* by an electron is proportional to its energy. In fact, the probability of emitting a *Bremsstrahlung* photon in a given path length is independent of the energy, as is also the *fraction* of the total energy taken by the average photon.

It is thus useful to define a cross-section, $b_{\text{rad.}}$, for the energy lost by radiation, by the equation:

$$-\frac{dE}{dx} = NEb_{\text{rad.}}, \qquad (5.3)$$

where N is the number of atoms of the absorbing material per cubic centimetre. At very low energies, where the interaction may be treated as completely non-relativistic, $b_{\text{rad.}}$ is independent of the primary energy. As we have seen above, the same is also true at very high energies where the screening is complete. From the point of view of studies on the cosmic radiation, this is the most important result, the value of $b_{\text{rad.}}$ being given by:

$$b_{\text{rad.}} = \frac{Z^2}{137}\cdot\left(\frac{e^2}{m_e c^2}\right)^2 \{4\ln(183Z^{-1/3}) + 2/9\} \qquad (5.4)$$

in this region. In the intermediate region, before screening becomes important, $b_{\text{rad.}}$ is given by the relation:

$$b_{\text{rad.}} = 4\frac{Z^2}{137}\cdot\left(\frac{e^2}{m_e c^2}\right)^2\left\{\ln\left(\frac{2E}{m_e c^2}\right) - 1/3\right\}, \qquad (5.5)$$

which rises with increasing energy of the incident electron. The variation of $b_{\text{rad.}}$ in water and lead as a function of the energy of the incident electron is shown in Fig. 22. The figure includes curves showing the cross-section for energy loss by ionization for comparison, and illustrates the effect of screening at high energies.

The cross-section for the emission of *Bremsstrahlung* by particles of mass other than that of the electron is given by formulae (5.4) and (5.5) multiplied by the factor $(m_e/M)^2$, where M is the mass of the radiating particle. Thus, the energy loss to *Bremsstrahlung* of all particles other than electrons is very small compared with the energy loss by ionization, even at the highest cosmic ray energies.

For electrons, the angle of deflection of the electron and the angle of emission of the photon are predominantly in the forward direction, both lying within a solid angle $\approx m_e c^2/E$. This angle is similar in magnitude to those found in the theory of pair production. As in the case of

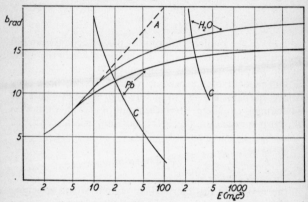

FIG. 22. The total cross-section for *Bremsstrahlung*, b_{rad}, in lead and water, as a function of the electron energy. b_{rad}. is plotted in units of $(Z^2/137)(e^2/m_e c^2)^2$. The curves marked C show the corresponding cross-section for energy loss by collision in the same units. (From Bethe and Heitler, *Proc. Roy. Soc.*, **146A**, 83 (1934))

pair production, the angle is not a unique function of the energies involved in the interaction, because the nucleus, within whose electrical field the interaction takes place, must take a small amount of momentum to conserve momentum balance.

Experimental data on pair production and Bremsstrahlung

Very detailed measurements on pair production and *Bremsstrahlung* exist only up to energies of some few hundred

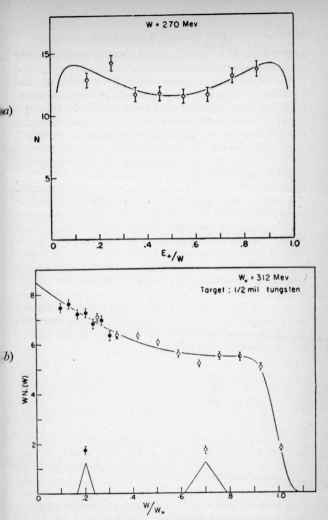

Fig. 23. Comparison of the experimental and theoretical differential cross-sections (*a*) for pair production by 270 MeV. photons, and (*b*) for *Bremsstrahlung* by 372 MeV. electrons. The latter curve has been slightly modified to take into account effects arising from the finite thickness of the target. (From DeWire and Beach, *Phys. Rev.*, **83**, 476 (1951))

MeV., while at higher energies there have been a number of cosmic ray experiments which have checked some specific points of the theory. In recent years a number of detailed experiments have also been made with machines to determine the differential and total cross-sections of both processes. The results of DeWire and Beach on the differential cross-sections of the two types of interaction, using 372 MeV. electrons for *Bremsstrahlung* and 270 MeV. photons for pair production, are shown in Fig. 23. At these energies excellent agreement is found between theory and experiment for both the differential and the total cross-sections.

A detailed knowledge of the angles of opening of electron pairs as a function of the energy of the initiating photon is of considerable importance in high energy studies, where multiple scattering measurements may no longer be useful. Several workers have studied the distributions of the opening angle of electron pairs created by cosmic ray photons in emulsions. A distribution, found by Baroni and his co-workers, plotted in units independent of the photon energy, is shown in Fig. 24. For a given photon energy, $h\nu$, Stearns has calculated the root mean square of the angle between the direction of motion of the photon and the emitted positive electron, and found:

$$\langle \delta \rangle = \frac{m_e c^2}{h\nu} . \ln \left(\frac{h\nu}{m_e c^2} \right) . f \left(\frac{E_+}{h\nu} \right), \qquad (5.6)$$

where $f \left(\dfrac{E_+}{h\nu} \right) \sim 1$ provided that $\left(\dfrac{E_+}{h\nu} \right) > 0 \cdot 1$, where E_+

and E_- are the energies of the positive and negative electrons respectively. The angle of the negative electron may be found by replacing E_+ by E_-. That the opening angle of the average pair is not given by adding together the mean angles made by the positive and negative electrons may be seen from Fig. 25, in which the opening angles of electron pairs have been plotted against their total energy. The mean value of $E_2/(E_1 + E_2) = 0 \cdot 24$, where $E_2 < E_1$

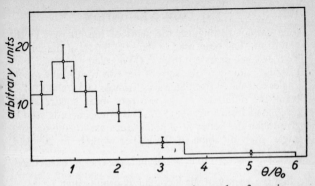

FIG. 24. The distribution of the opening angles of cosmic ray electron pairs plotted in units independent of the photon energy. (Data from Baroni *et al.*, *Nuovo Cim.*, **10**, 1653 (1953))

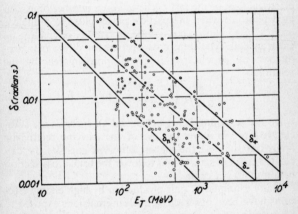

FIG. 25. The opening angles of electron pairs as a function of the photon energy

(one cannot distinguish the signs of the charges in the emulsion), has been used in the calculation of the curves. Two extreme cases are drawn: (1) marked δ_+, which corresponds simply to the sum of the two root mean square angles calculated from Stearns's formula (5.5), and (2) δ_-, being the difference of the two root mean square angles calculated from formula (5.5). This latter curve is seen to give much the better fit. Another formula for the opening angle, used by some of the earlier workers in the field,

$$\delta_n = \frac{2m_e c^2}{h\nu}$$ is seen to underestimate the energy, particularly

when the energy of the incoming photon is high.

Pair production by fast charged particles

Apart from the possibility of *Bremsstrahlung*, a fast charged particle may also create an electron pair directly † when it passes close to an atomic nucleus or an electron. The process may be understood in terms of the analysis of the electrical field of the fast particles into a number of associated photons; when the particle passes close to a nucleus each 'virtual' photon has a finite probability of creating an electron pair. The total cross-section for direct pair production by an electron is given approximately by the relation:

$$b_t = \frac{Z^2}{\pi 137^2} \cdot \left(\frac{e^2}{m_e c^2}\right)^2 \cdot \frac{28}{27} \left(\ln \frac{E}{m_e c^2}\right)^3,$$

when the screening is neglected, and all energies are sufficiently large to allow the use of the extreme relativistic approximation. At the highest observed energies the calculated effect of screening is to lower the total cross-section by about 10 per cent.

Many examples of pair production by high energy electrons have been observed in nuclear emulsions exposed to the cosmic radiation, and several attempts have been made

† The process is frequently called 'trident production' in papers on emulsion work.

to measure the absolute cross-section, and its variation with the energy of the primary electron. However, the data are at present rather confused, some authors reporting agreement between experiment and theory, while others report strong disagreement. Most, but not all, of the measurements in which the primary energy is under 10 BeV. show agreement with the theoretical values within the limits of error. At higher energies, the experimental data tend to show a larger cross-section than that predicted by theory. As a result of the small angles involved, and the high density of tracks, there is a danger of pairs, created by the conversion of *Bremsstrahlung* photons, lying so close to the track of the parent electron that they cannot be distinguished from directly produced pairs. But even when this effect is taken into account the cross-section seems to be at least a factor of five larger than that expected from the theory when screening is taken into account.

The angles between the outgoing electrons from a pair directly produced by an electron are of the same order of magnitude as those found in other electromagnetic processes of similar type, such as *Bremsstrahlung* and pair production by photons. On the other hand, the angles involved in pair production by heavier particles, such as mesons or protons, are of the order of magnitude $\sqrt{1 - \beta^2}$, where β is the ratio of the velocity of the incident particle to that of light. At a given primary *velocity*, the order of magnitude of the total cross-section is equal to that for pair production by electrons of the same velocity, so that such events are always very rare.

Cascade showers

A high energy electron traversing matter will, as discussed above, lose a large proportion of its energy in the form of *Bremsstrahlung* photons. These photons, in turn, will produce electron pairs, the energies of the electrons being of the same order of magnitude as that of the primary electron. The newly created electrons radiate further photons by *Bremsstrahlung*, which can create further electron pairs. In this way a cascade process is set up, the number of photons and electrons increasing as a function of the thickness of matter traversed, until the energy of the primary particle is dissipated among so many secondaries that the energies of the individual electrons are below the *critical energy*, where the rate of energy loss by *Bremsstrahlung* is equalled by that by ionization, so that they are rapidly brought to rest, or have little chance of radiating further photons of energy over the threshold for pair production. The process can, of course, equally well be initiated by a high energy photon.

As discussed above, the angular spread involved in the individual steps of the cascade shower production at high energies is very small, that produced by multiple coulomb scattering being very much greater. Thus, although photons which are not scattered are responsible for a large part of the particle path length in showers, the greatest contribution to the spread comes from multiple scattering. The high energy electrons will be concentrated in a narrow cone around the axis, while the lower energy electrons will be found spread out around those of high energy.

The longitudinal development of the shower, in which one considers the number of particles produced after the traversal of a given thickness of material, is, generally speaking, most important from the point of view of cosmic radiation studies, and it is just this aspect which has been most extensively studied. It is convenient to define a special unit of length in this connexion. This unit, known as the radiation length, L_R, is defined as that length in which a very high energy electron will lose, on the average, $(1 - e^{-1})$ of its initial energy. The quantity usually quoted refers to the high energy region where screening is complete and the rate of energy loss is proportional to the energy of the radiating particle. The numerical quantities for particular substances may be calculated from equations (5.3) and (5.4). Table 5.1 lists the radiation length in gm./cm.^{2} and cm. for a number of different substances. The mean free path for the creation of an electron pair by

TABLE 5.1

Substance	Z	L_R (gm./cm.^{2})	L_R (cm.)
H	1	138	15.4×10^5†
C	6	52.0	23.4
N	7	45.0	3.60×10^4
O	8	40.0	2.80×10^4
Al	13	26.3	9.74
Fe	26	14.3	1.82
Cu	29	13.2	1.49
Pb	82	5.90	0.52
Air		43.4	3.36×10^4
Water		43.2	43.2
Nuclear emulsion		11.8	2.95

a high energy photon, L_p, is of the same order of magnitude as the radiation length, and, in fact, it may be shown that the ratio of the two lengths is a constant for all substances, such that:

$$L_P/L_R = b_{rad.}/b_p = 9/7.$$

The statistical theory of the build-up and decay of cascade showers was first developed by Bhabha and Heitler, and, independently, by Carlson and Oppenheimer in 1936, and since that time many improvements have been made with respect to both the mathematical and the physical approximations. In Fig. 26 are shown curves, calculated for a number of different initial electron energies, giving the number of electron secondaries as a function of the thickness of absorber traversed. Curves are given for both photon and electron primaries. The calculations on which these curves are based involve two important approximations ‡: (1) the cross-sections used are those valid at

† Gases are considered to be at N.T.P.
‡ Called Approximation. 'A' in the literature.

H

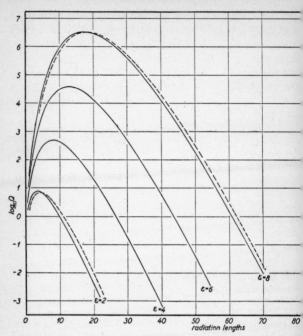

FIG. 26. Q, the number of electrons of energy $> E_c$, produced by a primary electron of energy E_p, where $\epsilon = \log_{10}(E_p/E_c)$ (smooth curves), and by a primary photon of energy E_p (dashed curves), as a function of the thickness of matter traversed. (From the tables of Janossy and Messel, *Proc. Roy. Irish. Acad.*, **54A**, 217 (1951))

extremely high energies, where screening is complete, and (2) the loss of energy by the electrons by ionization is neglected. At lower energies, where the cross-sections for the various processes vary as a function of energy, and ionization loss is important, the equations have not been solved analytically, but results have been published which have been calculated by the so-called 'Monte Carlo' method. This semi-empirical method is based on the use of a wheel of chance to study the fate of each individual particle of the shower. The only processes taken into account in all the above-mentioned calculations are ionization, pair production and *Bremsstrahlung*, and, at low energies, the Compton effect. No calculations have been made which take into account direct pair production, which, if the experimental evidence in the very highest energy region (~ 100 BeV.) is correct, may be expected to compete favourably with *Bremsstrahlung*. This might be expected to make corrections necessary at the beginnings of large showers, but would not play an important part in their later development, for the average energy of the particles of the shower, and the cross-section for direct pair production relative to that for *Bremsstrahlung*, both drop rapidly with increasing thickness of absorber.

The fluctuations in the average numbers of particles observed in cascade showers may, as has been pointed out by Messel, be considered in terms of what he calls 'fluctuations in effective depth'. For example, the distance which the primary electron or photon travels before it suffers the first radiative collision or creates an electron pair, is subject to very large fluctuations, and a delay introduced at this stage will be shared by all subsequent generations of secondary particles. For this reason, near the beginning or end of the shower, where the rate of change of the number of particles as a function of depth is large, the observed distribution is expected to be very much wider than the corresponding Poissonian distribution. On the other hand, near the maximum of the shower, where the rate of change of the number of particles as a function of depth is very slow, the distribution is expected to be Poissonian.

A very great body of experimental evidence on the properties of cascade showers has been obtained from experiments in which the multiplication resulting from the passage

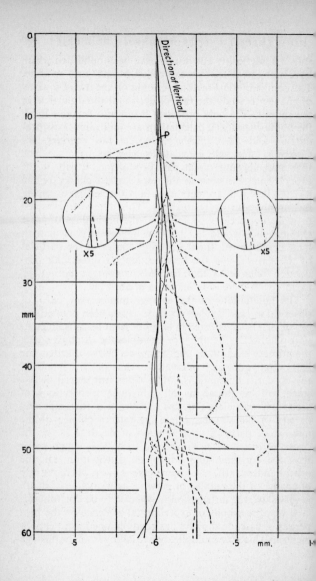

of a fast electron or photon through a lead plate of known thickness placed across the sensitive volume of a cloud chamber is observed. The results of these experiments, and others using suitable arrangements of counters, have provided satisfactory confirmation of the correctness of the theory up to energies of several BeV. One disadvantage of both the cloud chamber and the counter experiments is that one cannot distinguish the individual steps in the production of the shower. This particular disadvantage is not present in the nuclear emulsion, but, up to the time of writing, little really detailed work of any statistical weight has been done. Fig. 27 shows a projection of the tracks of a cascade shower observed in the nuclear emulsion. The lateral scale has been multiplied by a factor 20, with respect to the longitudinal scale, so that it is possible to separate the origins of the individual pair production events from nearby electron tracks. The rapid loss of energy of the particles from the first electron pairs may be clearly seen, as their multiple scattering is very much greater towards the tail of the event, than at the beginning, where they appear quite straight.

FIG. 27. Projection of the tracks of a cascade shower found in a nuclear emulsion. The lateral scale is multiplied by a factor of 20 with respect to the longitudinal. The energy of the initiating photon is 20 BeV. (From Hooper et al., Can. Journ. Phys., 29, 545 (1951))

CHAPTER 6

Unstable Particles in the Cosmic Radiation

During the past twenty years a considerable number of new unstable forms of matter have been found to exist. All the various particles so far discovered have been found to be produced in the very high energy nuclear interactions initiated by the primary cosmic radiation, and, in fact, it was in experiments on the cosmic radiation that most of them were first identified and studied. Later, as machines capable of accelerating bombarding particles to greater and greater energies have been built, an ever-increasing proportion of the work of establishing in detail the physical properties of the various particles has fallen into the domain of machine physicists.

A list of the elementary particles whose existence may be considered to be reasonably well established is given in Table 6.1, together with some of their more important properties. It is not certain that all these particles are distinct from one another, for it could well be that of the several different modes of K-meson decay which have been observed, some are merely alternatives competing with others already listed, but it is almost certain that the list will be incomplete within a comparatively short time. At the time of writing it is considerably less than a year since the existence of the newest particle, the anti-neutron, was experimentally established.

The μ-meson

The discovery in 1937 by Neddermeyer and Anderson, and, independently, by Street and Stevenson, that there exist particles in the penetrating component of the cosmic radiation at sea-level, which are intermediate in mass between the electron and the proton, was the result of a long series of experiments designed to determine the properties of the penetrating component. (See Plate III.) These particles, which were at first called simply mesons, or mesotrons, are now called μ-mesons, the Greek letter being used to distinguish them from several other sorts of mesons which have since been discovered. The original experiments showed that their mass lay between 150 and 250 m_e.

Shortly before the discovery of the particles in the cosmic radiation the Japanese physicist Yukawa had predicted the existence of a particle intermediate in mass between that of the proton and that of the electron. He had developed a theory of the forces between the nucleons in the nucleus which was based on an analogy with the well-known theory of electromagnetic forces. While the quantum of radiation which corresponds to the electromagnetic field (the photon) is massless, Yukawa found that that corresponding to the nuclear force field must be about 200 times heavier than the electron. This finite mass he showed to be a consequence of the short range of nuclear forces. Further, Yukawa found that it was possible to account for the β-decay of nuclei if it was assumed that the particles could be electrically charged and that they were unstable against β-decay with a half-life of the order of 10^{-6} seconds.

After its discovery, the μ-meson was quickly identified with the Yukawa particle, and a very large number of experiments were made to discover its further properties. In particular, experiments on the so-called 'absorption anomaly' showed that the particle was unstable, and that its lifetime was of the same order of magnitude as that predicted. It had been found that penetrating cosmic ray particles are more rapidly absorbed in an absorber of low density than in one of high density, but corresponding thickness of material in gm./cm.^{2} Kulenkampff had suggested that this effect might be due to the instability of the

TABLE 6.1
FUNDAMENTLA PARTICLES

Particle Name	Symbol	Mass (m_e)	Lifetime (sec.)	Decay products	Spin†	Strangeness	
Neutrino	ν	0	?		$\frac{1}{2}$	0	
Anti-neutrino	$\bar{\nu}$	0	?		$\frac{1}{2}$	0	
Photon	γ	0	Stable		1		
Electron	e^-	1	Stable		$\frac{1}{2}$		
Positron	e^+	1	Stable		$\frac{1}{2}$		
$\mu\pm$-meson	$\mu^\pm$	206.9 ± 0.2	$2.22 \pm 0.02 \times 10^{-6}$	$e^\pm + \nu + \bar{\nu}$	$\frac{1}{2}$		L-mesons
$\pi\pm$-meson	$\pi^\pm$	273.3 ± 0.1	$2.56 \pm 0.05 \times 10^{-8}$	$\mu^\pm + \nu(\bar{\nu})$	0		
π^0-meson	π^0	264.3 ± 0.3	$\leqslant 10^{-15}$	$\gamma + e^+ + e^-$	0		
τ^+-meson	τ^+	966.3 ± 1.9	$1.19 \pm 0.05 \times 10^{-8}$	$\pi^+ + \pi^+ + \pi^-$	1	1	Heavy or K-mesons
τ'^+-meson	τ'^+	967 ± 8		$\pi^+ + \pi^0 + \pi^0$	1	1	
κ^+-meson	κ^+	967.3 ± 5.5		$\mu^+ + \bar{\nu} + \pi^0$	1	1	
$K_\beta{}^+$-meson	$K_\beta{}^+$	963 ± 10		$e^+ + ?^0 + ?^0$	1	1	
$K_\mu{}^+$-meson	$K_\mu{}^+$	967.5 ± 2.2	$1.24 \pm 0.02 \times 10^{-8}$	$\mu^+ + \bar{\nu}$	1	1	
χ^+-meson	χ^+	966.5 ± 2.0	$1.21 \pm 0.03 \times 10^{-8}$	$\pi^+ + \pi^0$	1	1	
θ^0-meson	θ^0	965 ± 10	*See footnote below		1	1	}
$\bar{\theta}^0$-meson	$\bar{\theta}^0$	965 ± 10			1	-1	

			Stable?			Nucleons	Hyperons or Y-particles
Proton	p^+	1,836·12±0·02	Stable		$\tfrac{1}{2}$	0	
Anti-proton	p^-	1,824±51	Stable		$\tfrac{1}{2}$	0	
Neutron	n	1,838·65±0·02	Stable?	$p^+ + e^- + \bar{\nu}$?	$\tfrac{1}{2}$	0	
Anti-neutron	$\bar{n}$		$7·2\times10^2$	$p^- + e^+ + \nu$?	$\tfrac{1}{2}$	0	
Λ-hyperon	Λ^0	2,181·6±0·35	$2·85\pm0·2\times10^{-10}$	$p^+ + \pi^-$	I/2		−1
Σ^0-hyperon	Σ^0	2,326±6	Very short	$\Lambda^0 + \gamma$	I/2		−1
Σ^+-hyperon	Σ^+	2,328·1±0·5	$0·69\pm0·1\times10^{10}$	$\left.\begin{array}{l}p^+ + \pi^0 \\ n + \pi^+\end{array}\right\}$	I/2		−1
Σ^--hyperon	Σ^-	2,341·7±0·7	$1·6\pm0·2\times10^{-10}$	$n + \pi^-$	I/2		−1
Ξ^--hyperon	Ξ^-	2,585±7	$10^{-10}\text{–}10^{-8}$	$\Lambda^0 + \pi^-$	I/2		−2

* Since the discovery of parity non-conservation in weak interactions the situation is now (July, 1957) that one believes that there is only one type of K-meson, which is found in the states K^+ and θ^0, together with the corresponding antiparticles K^- and $\bar{\theta}^0$. A consequence of this scheme would be that K^+ and K^- have exactly the same mass, lifetime and analogous decay modes. With respect to the neutral K-particles one can say that those which are observed to *decay* are mixtures of the two completely degenerate states θ^0 and $\bar{\theta}^0$. There are two of these, one (K_1^0) of lifetime $0·95 \pm 0·08 \times 10^{-10}$ sec., which decays into two π-mesons, and one (K_2^0) of lifetime $10^{-8}\text{–}10^{-6}$ sec., which has various three-body decay modes. However, only the states θ^0 and $\bar{\theta}^0$ have a definite strangeness, and it is therefore one or the other of these which is produced in any particular *production* reaction. The produced particle is then a mixture of the two states K_1^0 and K_2^0, and will therefore exhibit both lifetimes. Many experiments have been designed to determine the spins of the strange particles but no evidence has been found for a K-meson spin greater than 0, or a hyperon spin greater than $\tfrac{1}{2}$. (See R. H. Dalitz : to appear in " Reports on Progress in Physics, 1957", Physical Society, London.)

† The sign '1' indicates that the spin is known to be integral (Boson), and '1/2' that it is known to be half-integral (Fermion).

‡ The decay scheme of negative K-mesons can only be observed when they decay in flight. At the time of writing all the decay schemes of K^+, except τ, have been identified.

penetrating particles, and that it could be used to provide a measure of their lifetime, for, in traversing the given thickness of matter of low density many of the particles would decay and appear to be absorbed. In traversing an absorber of high density, on the other hand, few of the particles are lost by decay, for the time of flight of a particle traversing an equivalent thickness of matter is very much shorter. Final proof of the instability of the μ-meson was obtained in 1940 when Williams and Roberts observed the decay of a meson, which had stopped in the gas of the cloud chamber, into a fast singly charged particle, which was apparently a positive electron.

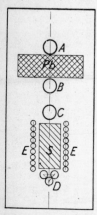

FIG. 28. A typical delayed coincidence apparatus to determine the lifetime of the μ-meson

More exact measurements on the lifetime have been made by the delayed coincidence method, both on cosmic ray and artificially produced μ-mesons. The principle of the method is illustrated in Fig. 28. Penetrating particles which stop in the block of material, S, are chosen by anti-coincidences between a counter telescope, ABC, and the counters, D. The secondary particles emerging with a predetermined delay are detected by the counters, E, with which the absorbing block is surrounded. By making counts for a suitable number of delay intervals of the proportion of the total number of stopping particles which produce a delayed coincidence, it is possible to determine the decay curve of the particles, and thus to determine their mean lifetime, the best value of which is now known to be $2 \cdot 22 \times 10^{-6}$ seconds.

If the identification of the μ-meson with the Yukawa particle is correct, then one would expect it to have a strong interaction with nuclear matter. This effect, which is at variance with the penetrating properties of the particles, could be tested by observing what happens when negative μ-mesons are brought to rest in matter. If the particles are strongly interacting, the negative particles, as distinct from the positive, will first be captured into a K-orbit about one of the nuclei of the stopping material, and will then be very rapidly absorbed into the nucleus. Most negative mesons therefore will not decay when stopped, and this effect will produce an apparent lifetime which is much shorter than that of the positive mesons, when measured in a delayed coincidence apparatus of the type discussed above. In order to provide a suitable source of particles of each sign, free from those of the other, Conversi, Pancini, and Piccioni used a magnetic lens in conjunction with a delayed coincidence set. The principle of such a lens is illustrated in Fig. 29. Two blocks of iron, F_1 and F_2, are magnetized in opposite directions perpendicular to the direction of the beam selected by the counter telescope. AB. In this way particles of the desired charge are focused, and may then be directed into a delayed coincidence set placed immediately under counter B. Using such an arrangement, it was found that the expected difference

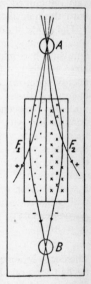

FIG. 29. The principle of the magnetic analyser

of lifetime was present when the particles were stopped in heavy elements, such as lead, in which nuclear absorption might be expected to take place even if the particles were rather weakly interacting, as a result of the fact that the K-orbit of a meson, being of radius only one two-hundredth part of that of the corresponding electron, is so small that the meson, once captured, spends most of its time within the nucleus. No effect was found when the particles were stopped in light elements such as carbon. Thus, it was necessary to conclude that the μ-meson had a weak interaction with nuclear matter, and it became very difficult to see how this property could be reconciled with the identification with the Yukawa particle.

The mode of decay of the μ-meson was not finally solved until the development of the electron-sensitive nuclear emulsion had made possible good measurements on very large numbers of examples. It was then found that the energy spectrum of the electrons was continuous from an energy of about 55 MeV. downwards, with a maximum intensity between 35 and 40 MeV. This result, taken in conjunction with the better value of the mass which was then available, suggested that two neutral particles of zero rest mass were produced in the decay together with the electron. They could be photons or neutrinos, or one of each. However, after a very careful search had been made by several workers for photons associated with the decay, with negative results, it was concluded that the neutral particles must be neutrinos, so that the decay scheme may be written:

$$\mu^{\pm} \longrightarrow e^{\pm} + v + \bar{v}. \qquad (6.1)$$

The decay scheme implies that the spin of the particle must be half-integral. From the fact that the cross-section for *Bremsstrahlung* by μ-mesons does not rise very rapidly at high energies, which shows that the spin must be less than 1, one can conclude that the spin must be $\frac{1}{2}$.

The $\pi^{\pm}$-meson

The theoretical difficulties, caused by the fact that the μ-meson could not be identified with the Yukawa nuclear force particle, were resolved by the discovery of the π-meson by Powell and his co-workers in 1947. Certain particles were identified in nuclear emulsions which had been exposed to the cosmic radiation on mountain-tops, which, after being brought to rest, decayed with the emission of another meson of comparable mass. It was possible to show by grain-counting and scattering measurements along the tracks of the mesons that the mass of the parent meson was about 1·3 times that of its decay product, which was emitted with a unique energy, and from which no decay particle was seen to emerge. The secondary particle was therefore tentatively identified as the μ-meson, for the emulsions in use in the original experiment were not sufficiently sensitive to record the tracks of electrons which might be expected to be emitted from the μ-meson decays. Later experiments in electron-sensitive emulsions confirmed the original identification. At about the same time, the same authors, and, independently, Perkins, identified other mesons of about π-mesonic mass, which sometimes emerged from a nuclear explosion in the emulsion, and which, on coming to rest, produced stars which suggested that the meson had been catastrophically absorbed in a nucleus. The fact that the frequency of occurrence of these events was very close to that of the π-μ decays in any given batch of emulsions led to their identification as the negative counterparts of the π-mesons. Further work established that π-mesons of both charges appeared to be directly produced in high energy nuclear interactions, and this fact, taken in conjunction with that that almost all π^--mesons appear to undergo nuclear absorption rather than decay, showed that the π-meson must have a strong interaction with nuclear matter, so that they could be identified with the nuclear field quantum of Yukawa.

The above conclusions of the cosmic ray physicists were rapidly confirmed in detail when it became possible to produce π-mesons artificially and in large numbers. It was shown first that they could be directly produced in nucleon-nucleon interactions for their production set in as soon as the energetic threshold corresponding to their rest mass was reached. The masses of the positive and negative mesons have been determined separately and have been found to be $273 \cdot 4 \pm 0 \cdot 2\ m_e$ and $272 \cdot 5 \pm 0 \cdot 3\ m_e$ respectively, and measurements on the lifetime have led to a value of $(2 \cdot 56 \pm 0 \cdot 05) \times 10^{-8}$ sec.

The fact that the μ-meson produced in the decay of the π-meson is of unique energy implies that only one neutral particle is involved in the decay scheme. Its mass, deduced from the ratio of the mass of the π-meson to that of the μ-meson, is found to be very small, so that it must be assumed to be either a photon or a neutrino. Searches for photons associated with the decay have led to negative results, so that one must assume finally that the neutral particle is a neutrino, and the decay scheme may be written:

$$\pi^{\pm} \longrightarrow \mu^{\pm} + \nu(\bar{\nu}). \qquad (6.2)$$

This scheme implies in turn that the spin of the π-meson is integral; the result is confirmed in more detailed studies of the interactions between π-mesons and nucleons, which further show that the spin is, in fact, zero.

The π^0-meson

The fact that, apart from the effects which can be directly attributed to electromagnetic forces, proton-proton, neutron-neutron, and proton-neutron interactions all appear to have exactly the same characteristics, has resulted in the formulation of the principle of the *charge independence* of nuclear forces. A consequence of this idea was the prediction of the existence of a neutral π-meson, and in 1947 Oppenheimer suggested that such particles, which he expected to decay very rapidly into two photons, might be responsible for the major portion of the electromagnetic component of the cosmic radiation at high altitudes.

The existence of the π^0-meson was first unambiguously demonstrated in a series of machine experiments by Bjorklund, Crandall, Moyer and York, who studied the angular distributions and energy spectra of photons emitted from a target bombarded by high energy protons as a function of the energy of the bombarding particles. The result was shortly followed by experimental evidence that similar particles were produced in high energy interactions of the cosmic radiation in which charged π-mesons were created. In both experiments the spectrum of the photons observed could be shown to be consistent with the assumption that they were the decay products of a particle which decayed in flight into two photons, and measurements of the maximum energy showed that the mass of the particle must be close to that of the charged π-mesons. Further experiments confirmed the decay scheme into two photons:

$$\pi^0 \longrightarrow \gamma + \gamma, \tag{6.3}$$

and detailed measurements of the photon spectra from the interactions

$$p + \pi^- \longrightarrow n + \gamma \tag{6.4}$$

and $\qquad p + \pi^- \longrightarrow n + \pi^0 \longrightarrow n + \gamma + \gamma \tag{6.5}$

showed that the mass was a little less than that of the π^--meson. Its best value is now quoted as $264 \cdot 3 \pm 0 \cdot 3\ m_e$. From the decay scheme it may be seen that the spin of the π^0-meson must be integral and even, for the spin of the photon is 1, and more detailed study of its part in various interactions has led to the final conclusion that its spin is 0, as is that of the charged π-mesons.

The measurement of the lifetime of the neutral mesons has proved to be a more difficult problem, for it is very short. Indeed, the first machine experiments set an upper limit to it of 10^{-13} sec., while the first cosmic ray experiments showed that it could not be longer than 5×10^{-14} seconds. At this stage Dalitz suggested, on theoretical grounds, that about one π^0-meson in eighty should decay by an alternative scheme:

$$\pi^0 \longrightarrow \gamma + e^+ + e^-. \tag{6.6}$$

In these events an electron pair is produced directly and its point of origin will be coincident with the end of the path of the π^0-meson. By searching for such directly produced decay pairs around very high energy events, in which the average energy of the π^0-mesons may be expected to be high, so that the relativistic time dilation is sufficient to lengthen considerably the path length of the π^0-meson in the laboratory system, and by measuring the distribution of distances between the centre of the nuclear explosion in which the mesons are produced and the first grain of the electron pairs, it is possible to show that the lifetime of the particles must be about 5×10^{-15} seconds.

K-mesons and hyperons

The first evidence for the existence of short-lived elementary particles of mass greater than that of the π-meson was published by Rochester and Butler at about the same time as the first observations of the π-mesons. These authors had observed two events in a magnetic cloud chamber, which they attributed to the decay in flight of a charged and a neutral particle respectively. They were able to show in both instances that the mass of the decaying particle was much greater than that of the π-meson. Two years afterwards the Bristol group published a photograph of an event which had been found in a nuclear emulsion in which a particle, of mass about 1,000 times that of the electron, came to rest, and decayed with the emission of three charged mesons, one of which was identified as a π^--meson. Very many similar events have since been studied, both in emulsions and cloud chambers, but it is only within the last two years that the experimental data on them have become sufficiently accurate to allow them to be classified. This progress has been greatly accelerated since the 'Bevatron' in Berkeley began to produce a beam of K-mesons early in 1955.

Today, the heavy unstable particles, or strange particles, as some writers now prefer to call them, are classified into two groups: the heavy mesons, or K-particles, and the hyperons, or Y-particles, which have been shown to have widely different properties.

Positive, negative and neutral K-particles have been

identified. Six different decay schemes have been determined for the positive particles, and three of these have been identified as occurring also for negative K-particles. The various established schemes are listed in Table 6.1. All the decay schemes are consistent with integral spin, and the masses of all the particles have been shown to lie within a few electron masses of $966m_e$ and to be consistent with this value. Thus, it is tempting to say that the positive and the negative K-particles can decay according to a number of different competing modes, but that they really merely represent two charge states of the same particle. However, there is some evidence which suggests that the spin and parity of the τ-meson, which decays with the emission of three π-mesons, cannot be the same as the spin and parity of the χ-meson, which decays with the emission of only two π-mesons,† as does the only well-identified neutral K-particle. Again, it is found that the negative K-particles are very much rarer than the positive variety; a fact which must be interpreted as a fundamental difference between the production processes of the two particles. K^--particles have, however, been observed to decay in flight according to schemes exactly analogous to three of those observed for the K^+-particles, the τ-meson, the χ-meson and the K_β-meson.

K-particles are lighter than protons, and their decay products are either π-mesons or particles arising directly or indirectly from π-meson decay. Like the π-mesons they have integral spin, and it seems very probable that they are in some way connected with nuclear forces. Hyperons, on the other hand, always have a nucleon or another lighter hyperon in their decay scheme, and have half-integral spins. They thus seem to be very much more closely related to nucleons than to mesons. Two experimental facts support this view. While in interactions in which no strange particles are produced, but only π-mesons, the number of nucleons is conserved, one finds that in those interactions which

† The discovery early in 1957 that parity is not conserved in weak interactions destroys this argument.

I

result in the production or absorption of strange particles, one cannot state a principle of conservation of nucleons alone, but must widen it to include nucleons plus hyperons. The second experimental fact is that in recent years a number of nuclear fragments have been observed to be emitted from stars during the evaporation process, which, after being brought to rest in the emulsion, disintegrate with a very large energy release, and sometimes even emit a π-meson. These fragments have lifetimes of more than 10^{-12} seconds, which is about 10^{10} times longer than one would normally expect for such a highly excited nucleus. However, assuming that a Λ^0-particle (see Table 6.1) is bound into the nucleus in place of a neutron, it has been possible to explain the long lifetime, the order of magnitude of the energy releases observed, and the distribution in energy of the π^--mesons which are frequently seen to emerge from the lightest of these 'hyperfragments'.

In a series of experiments, in which the interactions of π^--mesons of 4 BeV. kinetic energy in hydrogen were studied, several examples of the simultaneous production of a neutral or positive K-particle and a hyperon were observed. The reactions suggested for the interactions are:

$$\pi^- + p \longrightarrow \Lambda^0 + \theta^0, \qquad (6.7)$$

$$\pi^- + p \longrightarrow Y^- + K^+, \qquad (6.8)$$

where Y is an unidentified hyperon. In cosmic ray experiments, also, a number of events have been found in which a hyperon and a K^+-particle are produced in the same interaction, and the statistics of these occurrences is such that it is probable that the vast majority of hyperons and K^+-particles which have been observed to be produced in the emulsion could have been produced according to a reaction of one of the general types:

$$\pi + N \longrightarrow Y^{\overset{\pm}{0}} + K^{\overset{+}{0}}, \qquad (6.9)$$

$$N + N \longrightarrow N + Y^{\overset{\pm}{0}} + K^{\overset{+}{0}}, \qquad (6.10)$$

where N represents a nucleon.

On the other hand, no example of a K^--particle has ever been observed to have been produced in association with a hyperon. In fact, the only example of K^- production in which it could be shown unambiguously that another strange particle emerged from the same nuclear interaction was a star from which a K^--particle and a K^+-particle emerged. If, on the basis of this single event, one is bold enough to say that K^--particles are only produced in association with K^+-particles, then it is possible to explain the comparative rarity of the K^--particles in a very simple way. For, in interactions involving the production of a K^+-particle and a hyperon, the total energy which is used in creating strange particles is equal to the rest energy of the K-particle plus the difference of rest energy between the nucleon and the hyperon, which is much smaller than the rest energy of a K-particle. To produce a K^--particle in association with a K^+-particle, one would have to supply twice the K-particle rest mass, which implies that the threshold energy for the creation of K^--particles is higher than that for K^+-particles, and, in the cosmic radiation, the corresponding number of suitable interactions is much smaller. This is a result of the rapid decrease in the intensity of the primary radiation as a function of increasing energy.

When stopped in matter, both K^--mesons and negative hyperons are captured by the nuclei of the stopping medium and produce small disintegrations. It is characteristic of these disintegrations that frequently only a small proportion of the energy is seen as kinetic energy of the disintegration products, and that the number of prongs from the stars is small. In a number of instances another strange particle is observed among the disintegration products, and the low visible energy releases can be explained if one assumes that the absorption reactions are of the types:

$$K^- + N \longrightarrow Y^{\pm}_0 + \pi^{\bar{0}}_+, \tag{6.11}$$

$$Y^- + p \longrightarrow n + Y^0. \tag{6.12}$$

A very promising semi-theoretical classification of all the heavy unstable particles has recently been published by Gell-Mann and Pais. To account for the 'allowed' and 'forbidden' production and absorption processes, and the decay modes, they divide the relevant interactions into two classes, which they designate 'strong' and 'weak'. Strong interactions, which include the known forms of production and absorption processes for strange particles, are fast, taking place in times of the order of 10^{-22} seconds. Weak interactions are much slower and include the decays of the various particles. To each particle they now give a new quantum number, which they call the 'strangeness', S. This is a generalization of the isotopic spin quantum number, which has proved to be of great use in the study of the interactions between π-mesons and nuclei. They then postulate that in strong interactions the strangeness is conserved ($\Delta S = 0$), while in weak interactions the strangeness changes by one unit. By arranging the values of S given to each particle so that the well-established production and absorption processes are allowed, it was possible to make further predictions which could be tested by experiment. As a first example, the observed form of the reaction in which K^--mesons are absorbed (6.11) is such that one can conclude that if the strangeness is to be conserved, the K^--meson and the hyperon produced in the reaction must have the same strangeness.† If we now consider the production process in which a K^--meson and a hyperon are produced at the same time we find that in such reactions strangeness cannot be conserved, so, according to the theory, they are not allowed. This is in excellent accord with the fact that no K^--meson has been observed to be created in association with a hyperon.

† The assumed connexion between the strangeness and the isotopic spin implies that nucleons and π-mesons must have the same strangeness, while the fact that π-mesons can be produced either singly or multiply independently of other particles shows that their strangeness must be assumed to be zero.

A second success for Gell-Mann's ideas was his prediction that the Ξ-hyperon should be produced in association with *two* positive or neutral K-particles. Recently, a nuclear interaction has been observed from which a Ξ^--hyperon and two θ^0-mesons emerge.

CHAPTER 7

Degradation of the Primary Energy in the High Atmosphere

In the foregoing chapters we have investigated briefly the primary radiation which enters the top of the upper atmosphere, and have discussed to some extent the interactions initiated directly and indirectly by these particles. The question then arises as to whether it is possible to explain the observed variations of the intensity of the different components as a function of their depth of penetration into the atmosphere in terms of the individual types of interaction which have been discussed. A complete description of the degradation of the energy of the primary particles and their secondaries in their traversal through the atmosphere would, of course, require a completely detailed understanding of all the various processes involved; nuclear and electromagnetic. Such detailed knowledge is, as we have seen, not yet available. Further, the measurements on the intensities of the various components are only accurate to the order of about 10 per cent. Although it is therefore not possible or necessary at present to give a detailed quantitative account of the development of the cascade in the atmosphere, it is possible to give a rather simple, semi-quantitative, phenomenological account of its development in one dimension which is accurate enough to compare with the experimental results on the gross effects, and which at the same time is useful in that it is of assistance in obtaining a clear picture of what actually happens, and some knowledge of the relative importance of the various processes.

As a first approximation we consider all the primary particles which enter the top of the atmosphere to be protons, and assume further that in the nuclear disintegrations produced in the atmosphere no mesons heavier than π-mesons are created. The first may be justified on the ground that the interaction lengths of the heavy nuclei are short compared with that of protons, and they are very quickly broken up into their constituent nucleons after entering the atmosphere. The second assumption is based on the fact that only about 1 per cent. of all the mesons produced by the cosmic radiation are not π-mesons. (This assumption is not strictly true at the top of the atmosphere or at small latitudes. We shall consider a latitude of about 50° N. where the cut-off energy for vertical protons is about 2 BeV.)

The nucleon component

A number of authors, and in particular Messel, have in recent years developed a theory of the nucleon cascade in the atmosphere. The theory is based on the analogy of the electromagnetic cascade, and while it is not possible to make it absolutely complete at the present time because of lack of knowledge of the details of the individual processes, it is capable of giving reasonable agreement with the experimental results on the intensity of star-producing radiation as a function of altitude, provided that the experimental cross-sections for individual nucleon-nucleon collisions are fed in. Certain important results may be stated. The first of these is that at energies above the geomagnetic cut-off the energy spectrum of the particles maintains its shape throughout the atmosphere. This result is a consequence of the fact that the initial spectrum of the primary particles may be well represented by a power law.

The total intensity of the nucleon component in the energy region above 1 BeV. may be represented through most of the atmosphere by the relation:

$$N_N(\theta) = N_P \cdot \exp(-r\theta), \tag{7.1}$$

where the constant, r, is equal to $7\cdot9 \times 10^{-3}$ (gm./cm.²)$^{-1}$, θ is the atmospheric depth in gm./cm.², and N_P is the number of protons incident on the top of the atmosphere. An energy ≈ 1 BeV. is chosen as the lower limit, for mesons are only very rarely produced in lower energy interactions. Equation (7.1) involves an approximation at the top of the atmosphere which tends to cancel that made by neglecting the occurrence of heavy primary particles. This is because, with a cut-off at 2 BeV., some small depth of atmosphere must be traversed before there are produced particles with only 1 BeV. energy. Thus the intensity of the nucleons above 1 BeV. goes through a small maximum near the very top of the atmosphere. On the other hand, the heavy primaries behave in much the same way as a stream of individual nucleons with a very short interaction length, and a geomagnetic cut-off at only 1 BeV. per nucleon. Hence they tend to fill in the 'gap' at the top of the atmosphere.

The exponential decrease in the intensity of the nucleon component has been checked in a number of experiments in which star-producing radiation is studied, and has been found to hold within the limits of experimental errors.

The penetrating component

In making measurements on the intensity of the charged portion of the cosmic ray beam, it is usual to divide it into two components: the penetrating or hard component, which will penetrate lead without marked absorption, and the soft component which is rapidly absorbed in lead. It is usual to set the limit at 10 cm. lead, everything which penetrates this being part of the penetrating component, but different workers have used slightly different definitions and thicknesses of lead. For our purposes, it will be convenient to choose as the division a thickness of 18 cm. lead (200 gm./cm.²), for there are some good measurements of the variation with atmospheric depth of the intensity of charged particles which penetrate this particular thickness of lead.

In terms of the types of particles which are found in the

two components, the soft component will be composed predominantly of the electron-photon component of the radiation, together with mesons of energy less than 250 MeV. and protons of energy less than 500 MeV. The penetrating component contains all the high energy nucleon and meson components. As we have seen that the main source of photons in the cosmic radiation is the π^0-mesons which decay after being produced in nuclear interactions at the same time as the charged mesons, which subsequently decay to form μ-mesons, it is useful to consider first the generation of the hard component, and secondly the generation of the soft component and the variation of the total intensities with atmosphere depth.

The number of stars created at any given depth in the atmosphere by the nucleon component is very closely proportional to the intensity of the nucleon component itself, for the cross-section for star production is close to geometrical at all energies above 1 BeV. (Chapter 4). Thus the number of stars created in the layer of atmosphere between θ and $\theta + d\theta$ is given by:

$$[N_N(\theta)/L].d\theta, \qquad (7.2)$$

where L is the interaction length of the nucleons in air, which is assumed to correspond to the geometrical cross-section. Thus $L = 65$ gm./cm.^{2} †

The average number of mesons produced per star, n_π, has been determined experimentally in nuclear emulsions, and has been found to be 2·2 for stars with more than one shower particle, corresponding approximately to those with a primary energy greater than 1 BeV. This figure depends, of course, mainly on the interactions taking place in the heavy nuclei of the emulsion and might be expected to be

† Note the difference between the interaction length L of the nucleons in the atmosphere, and their absorption length $1/r$ (equ. 7.1) which is approximately equal to $2L$. The difference arises from the fact that the nucleons are not completely stopped in the individual interactions, but merely lose a portion of their energy, and at the same time knock-on other nucleons.

rather high when applied to air nuclei. However, at energies of the order of a few BeV., where the intensity of the star-producing radiation is greatest, there will usually occur only one inelastic collision in the struck nucleus, whatever its size, for the recoiling nucleons will have insufficient energy to initiate plural processes. In addition, we have learnt from the Brookhaven results that double meson production is important already at energies between 1 and 2 BeV. in single nucleon-nucleon collisions. Taking these two facts into consideration, it seems unlikely that the figure $n_\pi = 2 \cdot 2$ is a gross over-estimate.

The energy spectrum of the $\pi^\pm$-mesons originating in the stars has been well determined in emulsions up to energies of about 3 BeV., but for energies above this value there are no direct measurements. On the other hand, it is known that at very high energies the μ-meson spectrum at sea-level follows a power law of the form $N(E) dE \propto E^{-2 \cdot 7} . dE$. It is reasonable to assume that in the same energy region the spectrum of the $\pi^\pm$-mesons at production will be of the same form. At intermediate energies some information can be obtained from calculations on the intensity of the electron-photon component as a function of altitude, though, as we shall see later, this can only provide a very rough indication. The spectrum used in the following calculations is illustrated in Fig. 30.

When a very fast π-meson of energy, E, decays in flight to form a μ-meson, the energy of the μ-meson is given, to a very good approximation, by the equation:

$$E' = \frac{m_\mu}{m_\pi} . E = 3E/4. \qquad (7.3)$$

This assumes that the average velocity of the outgoing particles is the same as that of the decaying π-mesons. At high altitudes, where the density of the air is small, we can neglect the distance travelled by the π-mesons before decaying, for it is only of the order of 1 per cent. of the distance traversed by the μ-mesons.

Thus the number of μ-mesons of energy between E' and $E' + dE'$, created in a layer of atmosphere between θ and $\theta + d\theta$, is given by:

$$M(\theta, E')\, d\theta \,.\, dE' = 2 \cdot 2 N_\pi(E)\, dE \,.\, \frac{N_N(\theta)}{L} \,.\, d\theta, \quad (7.4)$$

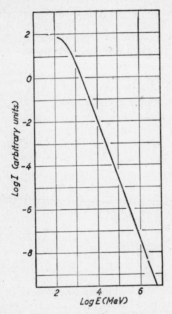

FIG. 30. The assumed production spectrum of charged π-mesons in the atmosphere

where $2 \cdot 2 N_\pi(E)\, dE$ is the number of π-mesons created per star with energies between E and $E + dE$. This is therefore the differential energy spectrum of the μ-mesons at creation.

At some distance, l, below θ, the differential spectrum of the μ-mesons at production must be multiplied by a factor,

$\exp(-l/c\beta B\tau_0)$, where $B = 1/\sqrt{1 - \beta^2}$, τ_0 is the rest life-time, and $v = \beta c$ is the velocity of the μ-meson. This factor accounts for those μ-mesons which disappear from the beam due to decay during the traversal of the distance l.

The relationship between h, the altitude, and θ is given by:

$$\theta = 1{,}033 \exp(-ph) \qquad (7.5)$$

where $p = 1\cdot44 \times 10^{-6}$ cm.$^{-1}$

Thus: $\qquad \log_e \theta = \log_e 1{,}033 - ph$

which leads to

$$l = (h-h') = -(1/p)(\log_e \theta - \log_e \theta') = \log_e (\theta/\theta')^{-1/p}. \qquad (7.6)$$

Using this relationship we find that:

$$\exp(-l/c\beta B\tau_0) = (\theta/\theta')^{1/zE'}, \qquad (7.7)$$

where $z = pc\,\tau_0 g$.

Equation (7.7) holds for all energies of the μ-meson so high that $\beta \approx 1$. The value of g is found from the equation $B = gE'$. If E' is measured in MeV., then the value of g is $0\cdot0098$.

We may now write down the number of μ-mesons of energy between E' and $E' + dE'$, created in a layer of atmosphere between θ and $\theta + d\theta$, which survive to reach a depth θ' in the atmosphere. This is given by:

$$M'(\theta, \theta', E')\, d\theta . dE'$$
$$= 2\cdot2N_\pi(E)\, dE . (N_P/L) . \exp(-r\theta) . (\theta/\theta')^{1/zE'} . d\theta. \qquad (7.8)$$

where E and E' are connected by equation (7.3).

The total numbers of μ-mesons of energy between E' and $E' + dE'$, reaching a depth, θ', is found by integrating over all production layers from the top of the atmosphere. We then have:

$$M'(\theta', E')\, dE'$$
$$= 2\cdot2N_\pi(E)\, dE . (N_P/L) \int_{\theta=0}^{\theta'} \exp(-r\theta) . (\theta/\theta')^{1/zE'} . d\theta. \qquad (7.9)$$

The integral (7.9) has been evaluated graphically for

15 values of E' and for values of θ' between 0 gm./cm.^{2} and 1,000 gm./cm.^{2} (This integral may, in fact, be reduced to an incomplete gamma-function.)

In the deduction of the expression (7.9) no account has been taken of the loss of energy by ionization suffered by

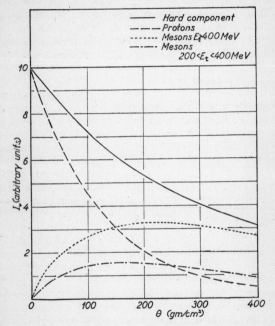

FIG. 31. Analysis of the penetrating component

the particles in traversing the atmosphere. For small values of θ', the error involved in this approximation is not great, for the amount of matter traversed by the average particle before it decays is small, owing to the attenuation of the atmosphere at high altitudes.

A second factor which has been neglected is the proportion of π-mesons which make secondary interactions in the atmosphere before they decay. This factor is a function of the lifetime of the π-mesons, their energy, and the density of the matter which they are traversing. It may be shown that at an atmospheric depth of ~ 200 gm./cm.^{2} the proportion of π-mesons which cause further interactions is ~ 2 per cent., and from many of these interactions the original π-meson, plus, in a few examples, further secondary mesons, will emerge, so that even here there is no catastrophic absorption. Thus the correction for the neglect of this effect is rather small.

To find the intensity of the penetrating component so that we may compare the calculations with the experimental results, we must add to the intensity of the fast μ-mesons the intensity of the *proton* component. At high latitudes Messel's theory of the nucleon cascade leads one to expect that the number of protons with energies > 500 MeV. at any point in the upper half of the atmosphere is very nearly equal to the number of nucleons with energies greater than 1,000 MeV. The rest of the nucleon component is composed of neutrons. The calculated variation of the proton and meson components as a function of atmospheric depth is shown in Fig. 31, while in Fig. 32 the calculated intensity of the penetrating component is compared with some experimental results due to Schein and his co-workers, from a series of counter experiments performed at geomagnetic latitude 51° N. The experimental results and the calculated curve have been normalized to each other at 400 gm./cm.^{2} No attempt has been made to extend the curves to atmospheric depths greater than 400 gm./cm.^{2} in view of the approximations involved in neglecting the ionization loss suffered by μ-mesons and protons in their traversal of the atmosphere. For the penetrating component this factor is not important in the upper half of the atmosphere.

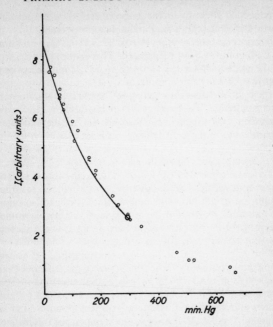

Fig. 32. Comparison of the calculated intensity of the penetrating component with the experimental results of Schein and his co-workers. (Experimental data from Montgomery, *Cosmic Ray Physics*, Princeton, 1949, page 163)

The soft component

We have already seen that the soft, or easily absorbed, component of the cosmic ray beam is composed of electrons, low energy mesons and low energy protons and other charged particles which have been produced as evaporation fragments from stars in the atmosphere, or are the result of loss of energy by the ionization of energetic particles produced higher up in the atmosphere. Of these various parts, the electronic is by far the most important.

Three important sources of electrons in the cosmic radiation have so far been recognized. These are:

(1) electrons which arise via photons of high energy produced by the decay of π^0-mesons.

(2) electrons from the decay of μ-mesons. When a particular initial electron energy is considered these tend to be produced at a much lower level in the atmosphere than those from source (1), owing to the long lifetime of the μ-mesons.

(3) electrons which are knocked-on by other fast charged particles of the cosmic radiation. The cross-section for the production of high energy electrons by this process is rather small, but it will be most important with respect to other sources at the bottom of the atmosphere and underground, where the density of the material traversed by the cosmic ray beam is highest.

One important point to note with respect to the electronic component of the cosmic radiation is that, far from being part of the primary radiation as was commonly believed until a few years ago, it is in each of its sources representative of the final stage of the degradation of the primary component's energy. Once energy has gone into forming an electron-photon cascade it is very rapidly shared among a large number of particles and dissipated as ionization energy in the atmosphere.

Electrons secondary to π^0-mesons

The number of π^0-mesons created in a given layer of atmosphere is half the number of charged π-mesons and the energy spectra are the same. The experimental evidence for this, and the dependence of the photon spectrum resulting from the decay of the π^0-mesons on the production spectrum of the mesons, have already been discussed in Chapter 4. After production the photons cascade downwards through the atmosphere, producing large numbers of electrons which dissipate the initial energy as ionization and in the production of further high energy photons.

The numbers of photons produced in a layer of atmosphere between θ and $\theta + d\theta$ by the decay of π^0-mesons may be written:

$$P(\theta) \, d\theta = G.\exp\left(-r\theta\right) d\theta, \qquad (7.10)$$

where G is a constant depending on the number of π^0-mesons created per star and on the actual number of stars. The spectrum of the photons we may calculate directly from the spectrum of the π-mesons which we have assumed in our discussion of the penetrating component. At a depth θ' in the atmosphere the number of electrons of energy greater than ε secondary to the photons formed between θ and $\theta + d\theta$ is given by:

$$P(Q, \theta, \theta') \, d\theta = G.\exp\left(-r\theta\right).Q(\varepsilon, \theta - \theta').d\theta, \qquad (7.11)$$

where $Q(\varepsilon, \theta - \theta')$ is the average number of electrons per initiating photon, with energy $> \varepsilon$, produced by photons of the assumed energy spectrum after traversing $(\theta - \theta')$ gm./cm.^{2} of air. Finally, we find that the number of electrons of energy greater than ε at a depth θ' is given by the integral:

$$P(\varepsilon, \theta') = G. \int_0^{\theta'} \exp\left(-r\theta\right).Q(\varepsilon, \theta - \theta').d\theta. \qquad (7.12)$$

The value of the function $Q(\varepsilon, \theta - \theta')$ may be calculated directly from the standard tables of the multiplication of electrons by the cascade process, provided that ionization is neglected. If this is done, and equation (7.12) is evaluated numerically, it is found that the intensity of the electrons falls off very much more slowly with increasing depth in the atmosphere than is indicated by the experimental results on the intensity of the soft component. This is because the value of ε must be chosen to be rather small (not greater than 20 MeV.) to conform to what is actually measured, and ionization plays a very important part in removing low

K

energy particles at all depths in the atmosphere, for the
critical energy in air is $\approx$ 100 MeV. Because particles of low
energy form a very considerable part of the soft component
at all altitudes the situation with respect to loss of energy by
ionization is fundamentally different from that encountered
in the discussion of the penetrating component.

Although the effect of ionization has been discussed by
Bhabha and Chakrabarty with respect to showers initiated
by electrons, there have been no theoretical treatments of the
effect of ionization on photon-produced showers. This was
at least partly a consequence of the fact that at the time
most of the theoretical work on the subject was done,
interest was centred on the hypothesis of primary electrons.
The calculations for electrons showed that at considerable
depths the effect of ionization was to reduce the number of
particles in the shower by a factor which could amount to
about thirty.

At depths of the order of several radiation lengths the
shower cannot 'remember' whether its primary was a
photon or an electron, and one would expect that the correction for ionization loss would be quite independent of
the nature of the primary particle. On the other hand, the
primary photons do not suffer ionization loss, and it therefore is unlikely that there should be any large correction
from this source in the first few radiation lengths. We shall
therefore assume that there is no correction, due to ionization loss, to the numbers of particles in photon-initiated
showers in the first two radiation lengths from their origin,
but that the full correction, as calculated for electron-
initiated showers, must be applied at all depths greater than
six radiation lengths from the origin. Between the known
curves at $\Delta\theta = 2$ radiation lengths and $\Delta\theta = 6$ radiation
lengths we can draw a smooth curve. The corrected and
uncorrected curves, calculated for the assumed photon
spectrum, are shown in Fig. 33.

Putting into equation (7.12) the function $Q(\varepsilon, \theta - \theta')$
which we have just obtained, we may calculate numerically

the integral in the expression. The resulting variation with altitude of the intensity of electrons secondary to π-^{0}mesons

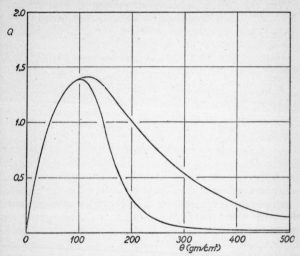

FIG. 33. The cascade curve before and after correction for ionization loss

is shown in Fig. 34. We will postpone the discussion of this curve until we have discussed the electrons which arise via the decay of the μ-mesons.

Electrons secondary to μ-mesons

At high altitudes the only other known source of electronic component that is of importance is that arising from the decay of μ-mesons. Electrons formed by knock-on processes form only a very small fraction indeed of the total intensity of the electronic component at high altitudes, becoming an important source only when other sources of soft component give rise to relatively low intensities and when the density of the matter being traversed by the cosmic ray beam is high, as at sea-level or underground.

The number of μ-mesons of energy between E' and $E' + dE'$ which decay in a path length dl is given by:

$$M'(\theta', E')\,dE'.\frac{dl}{c\beta B\tau_0},\qquad(7.13)$$

where $M'(\theta', E')\,dE'$ is defined by equation (7.9).

Now, $dl = d\theta/p\theta$, so that the number of decay electrons of energy between E'' and $E'' + dE''$, formed between θ' and $\theta' + d\theta'$, is given by:

$$S'(\theta', E'')\,dE''.d\theta' = M'(\theta', E')\,dE'.\frac{d\theta'}{zE'\theta''}.\qquad(7.14)$$

As before, we can now write down the number of electrons of energy greater than ε which are produced by the cascade multiplication of those from the decay of μ-mesons between θ' and $\theta' + d\theta'$, and by integrating over all values of E' we find:

$$S''(\theta', \theta'', \varepsilon)$$
$$= Q'(\varepsilon, \theta' - \theta'').\int_0^\infty \frac{1}{zE'\theta''}.M'(\theta', E').dE'.d\theta',\qquad(7.15)$$

where $Q'(\varepsilon, \theta' - \theta'')$ is the factor arising from the application of the cascade theory with ionization loss to the particular spectrum in question. The relationship between E'' and E' may be found from a consideration of the mode of decay of μ-mesons. When the μ-meson decays it forms one electron and two neutrinos of comparably small mass, so that, on the average, one-third of the total energy of the μ-meson component is acquired by the electrons which are formed. The shape of the energy spectrum at a depth θ' is obtained directly from equation (7.14).

We can now write down the total number of electrons which will be observed under θ'' gm./cm.^{2} atmosphere, integrating equation (7.15) over all values of θ' from θ'' to 0, obtaining:

$$S'''(\theta'', \varepsilon)$$

$$= \int_0^{\theta''} \int_0^{\infty} \frac{1}{zE'\theta'} \cdot Q'(\varepsilon, \theta' - \theta'') \cdot M'(\theta', E') \, dE' \cdot d\theta'. \quad (7.16)$$

Equation (7.16) has been evaluated numerically and the resulting curve for the first 400 gm./cm.^{2} atmosphere is shown in Fig. 34. It will be noted that the intensity of the electronic component arising from the decay of μ-mesons is very considerably less at the maximum than that arising from π^0-mesons, and that the maximum itself occurs rather higher in the atmosphere. Below the maximum, the intensity falls off much more slowly, and at 400 gm./cm.^{2} the two sources contribute about equally to the total electron intensity. Thus, at sea-level the electrons which arise from the decay of μ-mesons constitute by far the largest part of the total intensity of the soft component. In fact, it is possible to account for very nearly the whole intensity of the soft component at sea-level in terms of μ-decay electrons and their secondaries, and knock-on electrons and their secondaries, without considering at all those formed by the decay of π^0-mesons.

The energy spectrum of the electrons arising from the decay of the μ-mesons is markedly different from that of the photons arising from the decay of π^0-mesons, although the spectra of the μ-mesons and the π^0-mesons are very similar. At very high energies the spectra of the photons and their parent π^0-mesons can be shown to have the same slope if the initial spectrum can be represented by a power law. On the other hand, for the μ-mesons a power law spectrum of exponent $-g$ leads to a power law spectrum for the decay electrons with an exponent $-(g + 1)$. This is a consequence of equation (7.14), or, physically, the effect of relativistic time dilation. A second difference arises in the way the energy spectra vary with increasing depth in the atmosphere. The spectra of the photons from π^0-mesons can change very little, for the energy spectrum of the high energy nucleon component remains unchanged throughout the atmosphere, provided that the energies considered lie above the geomagnetic cut-off for protons, and that this is

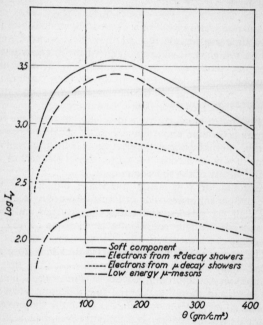

FIG. 34. Analysis of the soft component

of the same order of magnitude as that at which meson production becomes important. We have seen that these conditions hold rather well at northern latitudes. Direct experimental evidence comes from an experiment by Kim, which showed that the spectrum of π^0-mesons formed in nuclear interactions at an altitude of 4,000 metres was essentially the same as that observed by the Bristol group under 50 gm./cm.[2] atmosphere. Near the equator the above would not hold, for the geomagnetic cut-off is several times higher than the energy at which meson production becomes important. On the other hand, the lifetime of the μ-mesons is such that only those particles of low energy decay close to the place where they were created. Owing to the relativistic time dilation, energetic μ-mesons can travel several kilometres before they decay. Thus, the average energy of both the μ-mesons and the electrons arising from their decay increases with increasing depth in the atmosphere.

Comparison of the soft component with experiment

The soft component at high altitudes consists not only of electrons but also of low energy mesons and protons, which can be absorbed in 18 cm. lead by ionization loss alone. The number of protons remains comparatively small, because they are absorbed more rapidly than the mesons, and because the main source of production, evaporation from the nuclear interactions in the atmosphere, produces protons of low initial energy, the intensity of which will remain proportional to the intensity of the nucleon component. However, we neglect this contribution in the following.

The number of slow mesons as a function of atmospheric depth is shown in Fig. 34. This curve has been roughly corrected for ionization loss, for in the low energy region it plays an important role, even at high altitudes. In Fig. 35 the total intensity of the cosmic radiation as calculated is plotted together with the separate intensities of the hard and soft components. For comparison, the experimental points for the total intensity as a function of altitude, obtained by three groups of workers, have been added. These data have been analysed by Rossi, and the three sets of measurements have been normalized to each other at an atmospheric depth of 300 gm./cm.[2] Rossi's diagram also includes a curve showing the variation with altitude of the intensity of the penetrating component. As we have already obtained reasonable agreement between our calculations and experi-

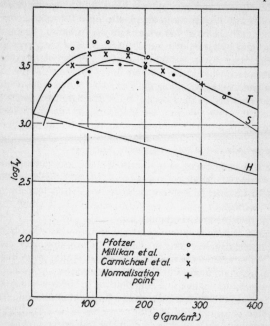

Fig. 35. Comparison of the calculated total vertical intensity (curve T) with experiment. The experimental results have been collected and analysed by Rossi, and are normalized to each other at 300 gm./cm.² The calculated curves have been normalized to Rossi's curve for the penetrating component (H). Curve S shows the calculated intensity of the soft component

ment for the variation of the penetrating component's intensity, we may normalize the calculated curves to the experimental points for the total intensity by normalizing the calculated curve for the intensity of the penetrating component to that given by Rossi.

The experimental points are very scattered, the difference between the highest and the lowest near the maximum being almost a factor of two. The curve which we have deduced fits satisfactorily the general trend of the experimental points, but it cannot be considered to be very accurate, for, due to the various approximations made in obtaining it (neglect of ionization loss by fast μ-mesons: approximation for the ionization loss by electrons: neglect of slow protons, &c.) and the coarseness of the numerical summations which have replaced the integrations, the curves certainly cannot be considered to be much better than 10 per cent. at any point. However, in view of the uncertainty of the experimental data, and the lack of detailed knowledge of the individual processes taking place in the high atmosphere, a very exact theory has, at present, little practical value.

It may be noted that the final altitude-intensity curve for the total radiation depends at high altitudes very strongly on those particles which are secondary to the π^0-mesons, and thus on the shape of the energy spectrum of the π^0-mesons and on obtaining the correct expression for ionization loss in the photon-initiated showers. The spectrum of the π^0-mesons is well known up to energies of about 1 BeV., from emulsion experiments at high altitudes, and for energies above 10 BeV. where its form will presumably be the same as that of the very high energy μ-mesons at sea-level. Very little is known about the precise shape of the spectrum between 1 and 10 BeV., and it is just in this region that the shape of the spectrum has the greatest influence on the shape of the altitude-intensity curves finally obtained for the soft component. Since the calculations were originally made, some evidence has been obtained to the effect that at energies greater than about 1 BeV. the spectrum of the π^0-mesons has the same form as at very much higher energies, the transition from a power law of exponent $-1\cdot5$

to one of exponent $- 2 \cdot 7$ at about 900 MeV. being rather sharper than that assumed in the spectrum shown in Fig. 30. This change would result in the electronic component from the π^0-mesons falling off a little more rapidly with altitude than is shown in Fig. 34. We have also remarked earlier that the apparently very large cross-section for direct pair production by fast electrons may involve modifications of the cascade theory at high energies, which would be expected to modify to some extent the curves which we have obtained.

General remarks

From the foregoing semi-quantitative discussion certain features stand out which are worthy of especial emphasis. In the atmosphere one can see, for instance, that the only important parts of the penetrating component are the nucleons and the μ-mesons. At high altitudes, very near the top of the atmosphere, the nucleon component has the greater intensity, but below a depth of 200 gm./cm.^{2} the intensity of fast μ-mesons becomes predominant, so that, near sea-level, almost the whole of the penetrating component is composed of μ-mesons, only a fraction of 1 per cent. being nucleon component. π-mesons never play an important part in the atmosphere at northern latitudes, for the vast majority of them decay close to their place of origin, so that their intensity at any depth is approximately proportional to the intensity of the high energy nucleon component at that particular altitude. In a thin material, such as air, where the number of nuclear disintegrations made by the primary nucleons, in a length comparable with that travelled by the average π-meson before it decays, is very small, the π-meson intensity will remain very much smaller than that of the nucleons. On the other hand, this equilibrium is upset if a dense absorber is placed in the beam, for, in the absorber, the path length of the nucleons to produce disintegrations is shorter than, or of the same order as, the path length of the π-mesons before they decay.

Thus, there results a high local density of π-mesons. A somewhat similar effect could be expected at the equator, where the π-mesons are produced with a higher mean energy, as a result of the higher mean energy of the primary particles. Owing to their greater energy, and the corresponding relativistic time dilation, their intensity with respect to the nucleon component will be higher than at northern latitudes, and the proportion of them, which initiates further nuclear interactions instead of decaying, will be considerably higher.

In the upper half of the atmosphere the electronic component which originates in the decay of the π^0-mesons makes the greatest contribution, not only to the intensity of the soft component, but also to the total intensity. These electrons are, however, rapidly absorbed, and as the intensity of production of π^0-mesons falls off with the intensity of the high energy nucleon component, there is little contribution from this source near sea-level, where the main contribution to the intensity of the electronic component comes from the decay of the fast μ-mesons which survive to reach this depth, and from the high energy electrons knocked-on by the μ-mesons.

The determination of the intensity and composition of the cosmic ray beam at any depth in the atmosphere can always be related directly to the intensities and energy spectrum of the nucleon component in the layers above that considered. In regions of high geomagnetic latitude, where the cut-off energy in the vertical direction is approximately equal to the energy at which meson production becomes important, the energy spectrum of the nucleon component is constant as a function of altitude, and the behaviour of the intensity very simple. These considerations do not hold, however, in regions of small geomagnetic latitude, where the magnetic cut-off is very much higher than the energy effective for meson production. Thus the energy spectrum of the π-mesons produced might be expected to vary as a function of the altitude at which they are produced, leading to alterations in the shape of the intensity-altitude curves for both the soft and penetrating components.

The measured intensities which have been discussed above refer only to the charged component. Owing to the experimental difficulties, there are few accurate measurements of the intensities of the neutral components. The photon component is intimately related to the electronic component with respect both to its intensity and its energy spectrum. The neutron component is related in a similar way to the proton component, and at high energies will behave in exactly the same way. At low energies, however, protons are removed from the beam by ionization, while neutrons can only be removed by nuclear interactions or collisions. Thus, neutrons are absorbed exponentially throughout the whole atmosphere, and some of those secondary to quite low energy primaries may be observed at sea-level, whereas protons would have been entirely lost by ionization. When the neutrons are finally slowed down to thermal velocities by repeated nuclear scatters, many of them may be captured by the process

$$_7N^{14} \, (n, p) \, _6C^{14}.$$

The density of C^{14} in equilibrium in the atmosphere is determined by the intensity of the radiation, and by the lifetime of the isotope, which is about 5,000 years. On the assumption that the intensity of the cosmic radiation has been uniform over the last 10,000 years, one can date the age of organic materials by studying the concentration of C^{14}. The relative concentration in the living material will be the same as that in the atmosphere, but after death there will be no further renewal, and the concentration will slowly diminish as the C^{14} decays.

The angular distribution

In the foregoing discussion only the intensity of the various components in the vertical direction has been considered. Considering in the first place only high energy particles, where the direction of the secondaries preserves approximately that of the primaries, one finds that two important cases arise. Firstly, there are those portions of the beam whose intensity depends only on the thickness of matter traversed (nucleonic component, and the electronic component secondary to π^0-mesons). Secondly, there are those portions of the beam whose intensity depends not only on the actual amount of matter traversed but also on the *distance* of the point of observation from the point of production (μ-meson component, and the electronic component secondary to it).

At an altitude corresponding to θ gm./cm.^{2} atmospheric depth in the vertical direction, the amount of matter traversed by a particle arriving from the top of the atmosphere at zenith angle ϕ is given by:

$$\theta'(\theta, \phi) = \theta \cdot \sec \phi, \qquad (7.17)$$

provided that one neglects the curvature of the earth. This relationship forms the basis of the so-called Gross transform, and it is sufficiently accurate for most purposes up to angles of 70°. For larger angles the earth's curvature must be taken into account, and equation (7.17) replaced by the more exact expression:

$$\theta'(\theta, \phi) = \rho \cdot \int_0^\infty \exp\left[- p\sqrt{(R^2 + h^2} \right. \\ \left. + 2Rh + x^2 + 2(R + h)x \cdot \cos \phi)\right] \cdot dx,$$

where R is the radius of the earth, h the altitude at which the direction is made, and $p \cdot \exp(-pR)$ the density of air at sea-level. p has been defined in equation (7.5). The density of the air is assumed, as before, to vary exponentially with altitude.

Using the above relationships, one may easily find the intensity at zenith angle ϕ and some given depth in the atmosphere for the particles which fall into the first of the two groups mentioned above, for this will be the same as the vertical intensity at a depth θ' instead of θ. To find the intensities of particles in the second group one must, however, recalculate the loss of particles by decay, replacing equation (7.5) by:

$$\theta' = \theta e^{-p'x},$$

where we now measure from the atmospheric depth θ, the distance above this in the direction ϕ being x and where $p' = p \cdot \cos \phi$.

For calculations of the angular distribution in the lower energy region, where the direction of the primaries is not accurately preserved by the secondary particles, one must have detailed information on the angular spread involved in the individual processes. There is a certain amount of experimental data available on some of these processes, but the actual calculations involved in obtaining accurate angular distributions to compare with those measured experimentally are very tedious, so that not very much work has been done along these lines. In general, of course, the angular distributions of the low energy particles will be rather similar to those of the higher energy particles, but will be smeared out by fluctuations of direction of the secondaries about the original directions of their primaries.

CHAPTER 8

Remarks on Effects at Sea-level and Underground

At sea-level the most important component of the charged cosmic radiation consists of the μ-mesons produced by the decay of π-mesons high in the atmosphere. These particles can reach sea-level only if their initial velocity at production is so high that there is an appreciable relativistic extension of their lifetime in the laboratory system (amounting to a factor 20 or greater, corresponding to particles whose initial energy is greater than 2 BeV.). Thus, the average energy of the penetrating component at sea-level is very much higher than at higher levels in the atmosphere, so that while the maximum intensity of the spectrum at sea-level occurs at a momentum of approximately 0·8 BeV./c., that found for μ-mesons at an altitude of 4,350 metres has its maximum intensity at a momentum of 0·2 BeV./c.

The only other component of the cosmic radiation at sea-level of major importance is the electronic component which is secondary to the μ-mesons, either by decay or collision. The intensity of this soft component is about 30 per cent. of the total intensity of the sea-level radiation.

The absolute intensity of the radiation has been accurately measured by many workers in northern latitudes† at sea-level, the best measurements being those for the penetrating component. Rossi has collected these various figures together and analysed them. He gives for the best value of the vertical intensity at sea-level and northern latitudes $(0·83 \pm 0·01) \times 10^{-2}$ particles/cm.²/sec./sterad. The intensity of the soft component is, as at higher altitudes,

† Above the 'knee' of the latitude curve.

usually measured as the difference between the total intensity and the intensity of the penetrating component. The exact value of the total intensity found depends critically on the experimental arrangement, and in particular on the thickness of the counter walls, for the lower cut-off energy for electrons will depend primarily on this thickness. Greisen has found a figure of 0.31×10^{-2} particles/cm.^{2}/sec./sterad. for the vertical intensity of the soft component above 5 MeV. Experimentally, the angular distribution of the radiation is found to be well represented by the function $\cos^2 \phi$, where ϕ, as before, is the zenith angle.

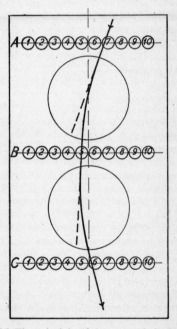

FIG. 36. The principle of the magnetic hodoscope

The energy spectrum of the penetrating component

The energy spectrum of the μ-mesons at sea-level may be measured either by measuring the deflection of the particles in a strong magnetic field or by measuring their absorption in suitable absorbers placed above the detecting apparatus. The Manchester group, for instance, have built a magnetic hodoscope for measuring the high energy end of the spectrum, the particle being detected by one counter in each of three rows separated by two large electromagnets (Fig. 36). Thus the curvature in the magnetic field may be measured, and the momentum deduced.

The observed differential momentum spectrum at sea-level and northern latitudes is shown in Fig. 37. There is a well-defined maximum near 0·8 BeV./c, after which the intensity gradually falls off as the energy is increased. In fact, it is found that between momenta of 2 and 20 BeV./c the observed spectrum is well fitted by a power law of the form $n(E).dE = aE^{-1\cdot9}.dE$. To measure the very high energy end of the meson spectrum, the earth may be used as a suitable absorber. Thus measurements of the underground intensity as a function of depth (which is always measured in metres water equivalent: m.w.e.) will provide information on the high energy end of the spectrum.

The experimental points obtained by a large number of authors are plotted together in Fig. 38. Several authors have attempted to draw two straight lines through these points, meeting at about 300 m.w.e., the slope above this point being $-1\cdot8$, while that below it is $-2\cdot8$. On the other hand, George suggests that there is in fact no real evidence for a discontinuity in the curve at 300 m.w.e. The effect is considered to be partly due to the increasing steepness of the μ-meson energy spectrum as the energy increases, so that the exponent increases from approximately $-1\cdot9$ at energies of less than 10 BeV. to -3 for energies above 60 BeV., and partly due to the additional energy loss by *Bremsstrahlung* and pair creation suffered by the highest energy μ-mesons.

L

The horizontal component at sea-level is in many ways similar to that observed deep underground, for the beam has already traversed 37,400 gm./cm.² air. Thus it is com-

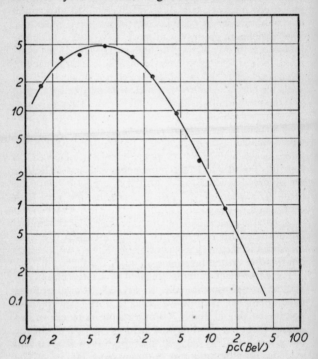

FIG. 37. The differential momentum spectrum of μ-mesons at sea-level. (Data from Wilson, *Nature*, **158**, 414 (1946))

posed mainly of μ-mesons whose initial energy must have been greater than 100 BeV. Lower energy particles would have been removed by decay very near the top of the atmo-

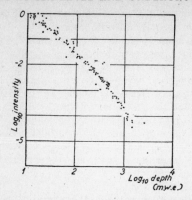

FIG. 38. The intensity of the penetrating component underground. (After George, *Progress in Cosmic Ray Physics*, Vol. I, Chapter VII. North Holland Publishing Company, Ltd. (1952))

sphere, for the distance travelled in this direction through the thin upper layers is very great indeed.

The temperature and barometer effects

One of the results of the finite lifetime of the μ-meson is the dependence of the sea-level intensity on the average temperature of the air above the place where the measurements are carried out. If the temperature is increased, without change of the barometric pressure, the density decreases, so that the average height of production of the mesons is increased. Consequently, more of the mesons will decay before they reach sea-level, so that there will be a decrease in the intensity of the penetrating component at sea-level. In principle, of course, it is possible to measure the lifetime of the μ-meson by studying this effect, but in practice this is very difficult, for it is first necessary to know accurately the temperature at all levels in the atmosphere, and secondly to know the energy distribution and intensity of the mesons produced in each atmospheric layer.

A second related effect which causes small changes in the intensity of the sea-level radiation is the so-called barometer effect. An increase in the barometric pressure at sea-level results in the beam having traversed a greater thickness of matter, with a corresponding increase in absorption due to ionization and the production of knock-on electrons, &c., in addition to the fact that the nucleon component produces mesons of some given intensity at a higher altitude than when the pressure is low. Thus the sea-level mesons not only have to penetrate a greater amount of matter, but they also have to travel a greater distance, with a consequent additional loss by decay.

The experimental values found for both these effects are of the order of magnitude predicted by theory, being for the temperature effect $(- 0.18 \pm 0.11)$ per cent./° K. (theoretical: $- 0.35$ per cent./° K.), and for the barometer effect $- 3.45$ per cent./cm. Hg (theoretical: $- 3.5$ per cent./ cm. Hg).

Janossy has suggested that these two effects might be of use to meteorologists in so far as they could provide an indicator of the variations in the temperature and pressure distribution of the atmosphere. The difficulty with this suggestion at present is that there are other causes of variation of the sea-level cosmic ray intensity which are not sufficiently well understood to be easily taken into account.

Time variations of the cosmic ray intensity

In addition to those variations of the cosmic ray intensity which can be traced directly to purely atmospheric effects, there are a number of other effects which appear to be of extra-terrestrial origin. All these variations which have so far been observed seem to be connected in one way or another with the sun, although it can by no means be established that the sun itself is the *only* source of the cosmic radiation reaching the earth.

The various effects may be divided into two classes: periodic and non-periodic. Of the latter there is one which has been shown to be connected with the occurrence of magnetic storms, which in turn are closely connected with the sun-spot cycle. During periods of severe magnetic storms the intensity of the sea-level penetrating component can be decreased by as much as 8 per cent., and can be correlated with the north magnetic component at the equator, which gives a measure of the magnetic storm field. Of particular interest is the fact that the decrease of intensity sometimes precedes the storm by two or three days. There also seems to be a general correlation between the sun-spot cycle of eleven years and the mean cosmic ray intensity taken over long periods, but the effect is not yet sufficiently well established to be taken as proven.

While observations on the hard component of the cosmic radiation at sea-level provide information on the high energy part of the primary cosmic ray beam, information on the low energy part of the beam may be obtained at sea-level by studying the intensity of the neutron component. If one studies charged particles one can only detect variations in the intensity of the primary radiation over some certain energy level, for the charged secondaries of lower energy primaries will be absorbed in the atmosphere by ionization loss, and will not reach sea-level. Neutrons, on the other hand, are absorbed exponentially, and variations in their intensity reflect directly variations in the total intensity of the primary radiation. Thus, by studying separately the various sea-level components one can hope to learn something about the energy dependence of the various effects, and this, in turn, may throw some light on their origins.

During the past twelve years there have been five large increases of the cosmic ray intensity which have been observed to be directly associated with the occurrence of large solar flares. The most recent of these, in February 1956, resulted in an increase of the intensity of the primary radiation of 50 times in the energy region 1–10 BeV., and 3 times in the energy region 10–100 BeV. It was also possible to show that the particles come from the sun, that their mean energy was about 4 BeV., and that they were predominantly protons. It has also been established that smaller increases are often associated with occurrence of smaller solar flares, and the average increase is of the order of a few per cent.

Apart from the non-periodic effects which have been discussed above, there also exist certain periodic effects, associated with definite time intervals.

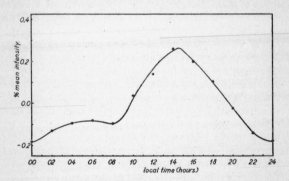

Fig. 39. The diurnal variation at Manchester, England. (From Elliot and Dolbear, *Proc. Phys. Soc.*, **63**, 137 (1950))

ated with definite time intervals. The most important of these, and so far the only two which have been definitely established, are the 24-hour, or diurnal, variation, and the 27-day variation. The most recent data on the 24-hour variation suggest that there is a peak in the intensity somewhat after local noon (Fig. 39) and that there is no marked energy dependence for the effect, for it may be observed with approximately equal intensity with widely varying sets of apparatus, some of which can detect particles associated with the high energy end of the primary spectrum

(~ 100 BeV.) and some of which detect those associated with the low energy end (~ 1 BeV.).

The second periodic effect is the 27-day variation, whose period thus corresponds with the period of rotation of the sun, as observed from the earth. This effect shows a strong energy dependence, being much more pronounced for those particles secondary to the low energy end of the primary spectrum. The variation is not strictly periodic, for it rarely

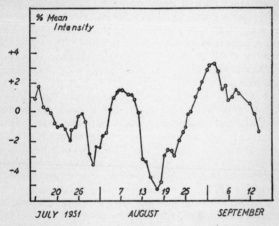

FIG. 40. A typical curve showing the 27-day variation. (From Simpson, *Proc. Duke University Conference* (1953))

extends over more than eleven cycles, and it is extremely irregular (Fig. 40). If the low energy part of the spectrum is included the effect can amount to as much as 30 per cent. variation between maximum and minimum in a single cycle, but is very much less pronounced for high energy particles, amounting, at the greatest, to 5 or 6 per cent. During the past few years (1951–3) the *average* maximum to minimum variation has been decreasing, possibly with the approaching minimum in sun-spot activity in 1955.

Interactions of fast μ-mesons

Owing to the very small cross-section for the process, the nuclear interactions produced by fast μ-mesons can most easily be studied underground where there are very few other particles to provide a background against which the events must be distinguished. Owing to the very rapid absorption of electrons secondary to the μ-mesons in solid material, very few of them will in fact be observed in the underground beam. In addition, it may be shown that the frequency of stars produced by fast singly charged particles in emulsions varies in the same way with depth as does the intensity of the main part of the beam, so that it has been concluded that most of the observed stars must be produced by μ-mesons.

The distribution of the heavy evaporation tracks from underground stars is very similar indeed to that observed at mountain and balloon altitudes, so that the energy dissipated by the μ-mesons in producing nuclear excitation must be similar to that dissipated by other types of star-producing particles. This is presumably because the μ-meson knocks-on a nucleon in the nucleus, which then shares its energy among the other nucleons in the usual way.

In addition to the evaporation tracks, shower particles are also observed to emerge from about half of the interactions. Of these, the 1_p events may be interpreted simply as the scattering of the μ-meson. The shower particles associated with the larger events seem to be most probably π-mesons, for scattering measurements have shown that some of them are certainly L-mesons (π or μ) and, in addition, slow π-mesons have been observed in plates poured, exposed, and developed deep underground, so that it is quite certain that they must have been produced locally.

It may be shown that the production of π-mesons by fast μ-mesons might be expected to take place in high energy collisions. It is known that π-mesons can be produced by photons with a cross-section $\sim 10^{-28}$ cm.^{2} per nucleon. If one then considers the field of a fast μ-meson to be composed of a stream of virtual photons (for comparison, see page 102) one can calculate the expected cross-section and compare this with that actually observed. As the mean energy of the μ-mesons increases with increasing depth underground, the apparent cross-section should increase with increasing depth. This effect has indeed been found, and the experimental results of George and Evans are compared with the theoretically calculated values in Table 8.1.

TABLE 8.1

Depth m.w.e.	Observed cross-section $(10^{-35}$ cm.^{2}/nucleon$)$	Calculated cross-section $(10^{-30}$ cm.^{2}/nucleon$)$	Ratio $\dfrac{observed}{calculated}$
20	$4 \cdot 2 \pm 0 \cdot 7$	$2 \cdot 9$	$1 \cdot 45 \pm 0 \cdot 24$
34	$4 \cdot 5 \pm 1 \cdot 2$	$3 \cdot 5$	$1 \cdot 3 \pm 0 \cdot 33$
60	$5 \cdot 3 \pm 1 \cdot 7$	$4 \cdot 1$	$1 \cdot 3 \pm 0 \cdot 4$

The above theoretical values are based on a rough estimate of the cross-section for photons from machine work at Berkeley. The validity of such a semi-theoretical estimate (the photon cross-section was measured up to energies of only a few hundred MeV.) is borne out by the rather good agreement found in Table 8.1. The study of underground stars therefore provides a means of studying the cross-section for the production of π-mesons and stars by photons.

Extensive air showers

When it was still believed that the primary cosmic radiation consisted of electrons or photons it was shown that, from the theory of cascade showers, one would expect that those showers produced by the high energy tail of the primary energy spectrum would reach sea-level directly, and that they would be recognizable because they would produce coincidences in counters spaced several metres apart. That such showers indeed exist and can be observed at sea-level was rapidly confirmed by various workers who measured the coincidence rate between two or more counters as a function of the lateral distance between them. The early results of Auger and his collaborators are shown in Fig. 41. However, during the past few years the interpretation of these events has had to be radically revised; firstly, because, as has been remarked earlier, it is now known that the primary radiation is not electronic, and secondly, because

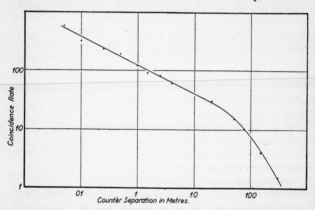

FIG. 41. The frequency of extensive air showers as a function of counter separation. (From Auger *et al.*, *C.R. Acad. Paris*, **208**, 1641 (1939))

it has been found that in addition to the electronic component of such showers, which was proved to exist by adding a cloud chamber containing a lead plate to the extensive shower sets, there exists a penetrating component, which is mainly composed of μ-mesons with a small admixture of nucleons.

Today, these showers are explained as having been initiated by very high energy protons or heavy nuclei with energies of the order of 10^4 BeV./nucleon or greater. Total energies as great as 10^{10} BeV. (~ 1 joule concentrated in a single particle!) have been observed. Such events, which are very rare, give rise to millions of secondary particles, and the lateral spread may be of the order of a kilometre. The effective absorption length for nucleons in the first few generations of the showers is very considerably greater than twice the interaction length, for, even assuming that the individual nucleon-nucleon collisions are completely inelastic, the velocity of the centre of mass system is so great that after the first collision both the primary particle and the knock-on have energies which are still very high compared with those considered in the more normal course of events. Thus the nucleons produce considerably more than two interactions each in the first generations of the shower, as do their immediate nucleon secondaries. In addition, the π-mesons created in the first interactions will have very high energies and will have more chance of interacting and producing further knock-on nucleons than of decaying, owing to the very great relativistic extension of their lifetime in the laboratory system, and their consequently very much longer path length through the atmosphere before they decay.

Taking into account these special considerations due to the very high energy of the primary particle, the development of the shower will follow closely the lines indicated in Chapter 7 for the degradation of the energy in the atmosphere, though it is also possible that, at such high energies, other processes, such as the creation of a considerable proportion of mesons heavier than π-mesons, and also possibly nucleon-antinucleon pairs, should be taken into account. Both detailed calculations of the process, and a detailed investigation of the lateral structure of these showers as a function of the altitude of observation, have still to be made, and it is as yet too early to say just how much information on the various processes taking place in their development can be obtained from their direct study.

For an up-to-date and detailed account of extensive air showers the reader is referred to a review published by Greisen in Wilson's *Progress in Cosmic Ray Physics*, Vol. III.

Further Reading

General

WILSON, J. G. (Editor). *Progress in Cosmic Ray Physics.*
Vols. I, II and III. North Holland Publishing Company (1952, 1954 and 1956)

HEISENBERG, W. (Editor). *Vortrage über Kosmische Strahlung.* Springer Verlag, Berlin (1953)

The above four volumes contain up-to-date review articles by specialists in a large number of different fields within the study of the cosmic radiation, and have excellent bibliographies.

DAUVILLIER, A. *Les Rayons Cosmiques.* Dunod, Paris (1954)

An excellent general account of the cosmic radiation, and the experimental techniques involved in its study.

ROSSI, B. *Rev. Mod. Phys.*, **20**, 537 (1948)

A review and analysis of the data on the degradation of energy of the primary particles in the atmosphere. It contains a representative bibliography to much of the earlier work.

ROSSI, B. *High Energy Particles.* Prentice Hall, New York (1952)

Contains accounts of high energy electromagnetic and nuclear interactions, and of the most important experimental techniques.

On π- and μ-mesons and high energy nuclear interactions

MARSHAK, R. *Meson Physics.* McGraw-Hill, New York (1952)

BETHE, H. A. and DE HOFFMANN, F. *Mesons and Fields*. Vol. II. Row, Peterson and Company, New York (1955)

Electromagnetic interactions and quantum electrodynamics

SPRING, K. H. *Photons and Electrons*. These Monographs (1950)

HEITLER, W. *Quantum Theory of Radiation*. 3rd Edition. Oxford University Press (1954)

Theory of geomagnetic effects

JOHNSON, T. H. *Rev. Mod. Phys.*, **10,** 193 (1938)

Detailed accounts of much of the basic theory of the subject (collision processes, cascade showers, geomagnetic effects, atmospheric effects, &c.) can be found in the earlier books. In particular see:

JANOSSY, L. *Cosmic Rays*. Oxford University Press (1948)

MONTGOMERY, D. J. X. *Cosmic Ray Physics*. Princeton University Press (1949)

Range-Energy Relation

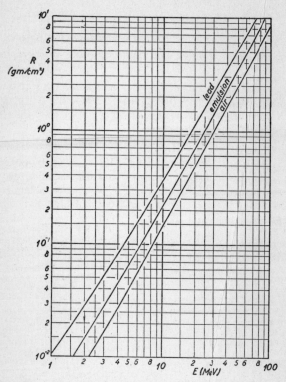

Fig. 42(a). Range-energy curves for protons in air, emulsion and lead

Range-Energy Relation

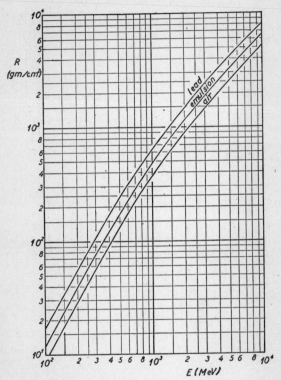

Fig. 42(b). Range-energy curves for protons in air, emulsion and lead

Index